Penguin Books
Britain's Poisoned Water

Frances Craig is a travel writer and freelance journalist specializing in environmental issues. Phil Craig is a television producer and journalist. He has worked for the BBC's *Brass Tacks* and for Granada Television's *World in Action*, for which he researched a special investigation into British drinking-water quality. They live in Manchester with their two children.

BRITAIN'S POISONED WATER

Frances Craig and Phil Craig

PENGUIN BOOKS

Published by the Penguin Group
27 Wrights Lane, London w8 5tz, England
Viking Penguin Inc., 40 West 23rd Street, New York, New York 10010, USA
Penguin Books Australia Ltd, Ringwood, Victoria, Australia
Penguin Books Canada Ltd, 2801 John Street, Markham, Ontario, Canada l3r 1b4
Penguin Books (NZ) Ltd, 182–190 Wairau Road, Auckland 10, New Zealand

Penguin Books Ltd, Registered Offices: Harmondsworth, Middlesex, England

First published 1989
10 9 8 7 6 5 4 3 2 1

Made and printed in Great Britain by
Richard Clay Ltd, Bungay, Suffolk
Filmset in Monophoto Sabon

For Alex and Helen

CONTENTS

ACKNOWLEDGEMENTS

In 1987 Phil met Andy Booth of Greenpeace to discuss an idea for a *World in Action* report on river pollution. After listening to what Andy had to say, he came away wanting to investigate drinking-water pollution instead. Having done so, he cut Andy Booth's interview out of the finished programme. In delayed atonement Andy and his colleagues Tim Birch and Beverley Thorpe head our thank-you list.

Close behind come Andrew Lees and his team at Friends of the Earth, who provided us with invaluable and patient assistance. We are also grateful to Ray Fitzwalter at Granada Television for permission to use information gathered on behalf of *World in Action*.

In addition we wish to thank the following for their time and their trouble: Dr Michael Moore, Ken Stewart, Dr David Wheeler, Tony Davies, Fred Pearce, Dr John Ashton, Chris Bryer, Professor Derek Bryce-Smith, Anne Scott, David Boyd, Chris Murphy, Freddie Drabble, Margaret Taylor, Tom Franklin, Andrew Watterson, Noreen Miller, Dr Christopher Martin, Dr Neil Ward, Paul Couling, Peter Snell, Dr Gabriel Scally Jr, Dr Alistair Hay, Chris Malone, Barbara Cummins, Charles Tremayne, Mike Lennon, P. Clavell Blount, Stuart Crocker, Professor Norman Moore, Robin Grove-White, Reg Green, Geoff Williams, Jim Wild, Bob Harris, Douglas Cross, Richard Palmer, Pat Gowan and the Granada newsroom.

Finally we would like to express our gratitude to all the officials, managers and inspectors who assisted us but felt it would be best if we did not name them on this page.

F.C.
P.C.
March 1989

INTRODUCTION

When you've spent half your political life dealing with humdrum issues like the environment . . . it's exciting to have a real crisis on your hands.

Margaret Thatcher, during the Falklands campaign, 1982

Our biggest problem in writing this book has been repetition. There are only so many times you can use words like 'disgraceful', 'scandalous', 'dangerous', 'squalid'. Our thesaurus is well thumbed, but the same expressions keep coming back. One word above all: 'crisis'.

Our water environment is in crisis because it is carelessly polluted and weakly protected. Agriculture and industry combine to flood our rivers with chemicals. Our decaying sewage system, designed in the nineteenth century, struggles to cope with the pollution of the twentieth. We pump into our seas raw sewage that washes back on to our beaches. Leakages of concentrated animal waste drive out the oxygen and the life from our rivers. Toxic rubbish from Britain and abroad is dumped into holes in the ground, from which it leaks to pollute our water sources. There is poison in the pipes too – lead, the dangers of which are only now being fully understood. And there's aluminium, added by the water authorities themselves yet strongly suspected of causing a cruel brain disease.

Those who are charged with preserving our environment and protecting our health have manifestly failed in their duty. Political priorities have overridden considerations of water quality. We have spoken to dozens of frustrated men and women employed in the water industry and engaged in what passes for environmental protection in this country. Some are inspectors who feel impotent in the face of illegal pollution and dumping; some are water-authority employees who have seen quality decline as their organizations have been fattened up for privatization. Over the last decade the government's attitude has seemed to be one of indifference, inactivity, even outright connivance with the polluter. European anti-pollution laws are evaded or simply ignored. Reports, Royal Commissions and recommendations gather dust on Whitehall shelves. When established pollution standards cannot be met, the standards are conveniently changed. Yet at all times the public is assured that there is nothing wrong with the water.

But there is something wrong with the water, this most precious of all natural resources. In this book we intend to examine the patterns of neglect and mismanagement that have brought this situation about. Until recently most people thought of declining water quality, if they thought about it at all, in terms of dead streams or sewage washed up on beaches. These issues are certainly important, but they have not been sufficient to provoke mass protest. Now, however, the problem of water quality is coming home to every one of us through our very own kitchen taps. Millions of families are drinking water containing levels of toxic chemicals that are frequently far in excess of international standards. Our aim is to chart the crisis of Britain's water environment as it affects rivers, the sea and our countryside and, most important, as it affects the water coming out of our taps.

If pressed, government ministers will concede that Britain's water system needs urgent attention. Privatization has been offered as the answer. Private water, we are told, will mean cleaner water. Whether you accept this proposition depends on your faith in the ability of private companies to control a priceless national asset. There will be public watchdogs, but will they be able to bite? Past experience of the private waste-disposal industry suggests that commercial pressures and environmental protection do not mix. Companies inevitably strive to maximize their profits, and there is always a temptation to bend the rules. The regulatory agencies, starved of resources, complain bitterly that the cowboys run rings around them.

As we go to press the whole privatization scheme appears to be threatened by Britain's failure to meet EEC standards for drinking- and bathing-water cleanliness. The EEC Commissioner is questioning the right of the British government to grant exemptions from current EEC pollution limits – limits that carry the force of European law. The government and the water industry have already unleashed an unprecedented multi-million-pound publicity barrage to persuade us to buy water shares. City analysts warn, however, that the share issue could flop completely if Brussels insists that Britain clean up its water fast. Such an operation would add hundreds of millions of pounds to the spending plans of the new water companies and could send their profits and shares into a tailspin. Those of us who are concerned about the parlous state of our water environment can only be grateful that EEC officials seem more concerned about our welfare than does our own government.

Of course, water is not a glamorous product. We wash our cars with it and flush it down our toilets. All pretty humdrum stuff. It is difficult to stir up much popular enthusiasm for the defence of sewage-treatment standards or to get people on to the streets to protest about the evasion of some obscure EEC regulation concerning nitrate contamination. Yet our national water resources are critical for public health and for the future of our environment.

Those who have never been particularly concerned about water quality may find some examples of the current crisis almost incredible. Over 350 different man-made chemicals have now been detected in British tap water. Lead in drinking water is markedly reducing the intelligence of hundreds of thousands of British children. There were 23,253 recorded water-pollution incidents in 1988; 1 per cent of them ended in prosecution. In 1987 there were five hazardous-waste inspectors to oversee 5,600 waste sites; they managed to visit 225. As waste imports soar, Britain is becoming known as a soft touch for disposing of other countries' toxic rubbish. One in five sewage-treatment works breaks the laws controlling waste discharges. A group of Cornish doctors warned holidaymakers in the mid-1980s to inoculate themselves against polio and typhoid before visiting some local beaches because so much human excrement was being washed ashore. Typhoid inoculations? For a holiday in Cornwall? It sounds more like the advice you might expect if you were planning a trip to Bangladesh.

The quotation from Mrs Thatcher with which we opened this introduction may be a little unfair. A war is, after all, a very pressing business. But the choice of words is interesting. The environment is indeed a humdrum issue to many politicians, and few people vote on the basis of their tap water. The Prime Minister enjoys the occasional Cornish holiday. If she wants to enjoy her morning walk along the sand without any unpleasant encounters at the shoreline, and if she wants the British people to have cleaner and safer drinking water, we hope that she might instruct her ministers to address some of the humdrum, and not so humdrum, issues raised in the following pages.

I

FRESH FIELDS AND POISONS NEW

Agriculture and water pollution

The farming fraternity must realize that the land may be theirs but the underground water is not.
  Tony Davies, former director of Anglian Water Authority, 1987

The farmers might well ask: 'Where's the pile of bodies?' but our view is that by the time there's a pile of bodies, it's far too late.
  Andrew Lees, Friends of the Earth, 1988

A word in the minister's ear: modern agriculture and the farming lobby

At school they taught us about 'Turnip' Townsend, the great farming reformer of the eighteenth century. Townsend pioneered the four-course crop rotation and laid down a pattern of land-use for centuries to come. A field might grow wheat one year and turnips the next, lie fallow for another year and be used as grazing for a fourth. It would then return to wheat. Crop rotation preserved the fertility of the land for the generations that followed, but it did not produce anything like as much grain as today's dominant monocultures in which farmers grow the same crop in the same field year after year.

They do it by using chemicals, thousands of tonnes of them. That's the only way it can be done. The same crop, grown repeatedly on the same land, depletes the nutrients in the soil, which won't grow anything satisfactorily unless you spread fertilizer on it. And to protect your investment you need a liberal application of pesticides and herbicides. Ever since the food shortages of the Second World War Britain's farmers have been encouraged to boost production. 'Increase the yields of all your fields,' proclaimed Whitehall in 1941. 'More fertilizer means more food.' With national self-sufficiency in food as the objective, £100 billion of public money have poured into agriculture since those days, resulting in a dramatic increase in overall food production, more land given over to arable farming and a leap in the amount of grain that can be produced from a given hectare of soil.

The normal rules of supply and demand have been bent to encourage this unprecedented expansion in agricultural production. Even in the harsh economic conditions of the 1980s agriculture has kept its protected place. Uneconomic coal mines and shipyards are closed because of 'market forces', but British farming still enjoys a singularly privileged position within the national economy. A levy on imported grain ensures that arable production is not challenged by cheap imports. Farmers know that the prices they receive are normally guaranteed and that an elaborate system of subsidies, grants and fiscal exemptions underpins their entire rural economy. As it stands the system produces overpriced food, which is a covert tax on consumers, and surpluses, which have to be bought, stored or disposed of at great expense. In 1984 the EEC destroyed 5,000 oranges, 5,000 lemons and 40 cauliflowers for every minute of the year. Such a system of agriculture also penalizes farming in poorer continents and thus contributes further to their underdevelopment.

In times of war and food rationing intensive farming is understandable, but many people now believe that subsidized agricultural overproduction is no longer in the interests of the British people and that it poses a threat to both the environment and public health. In particular, modern farm practice is causing widespread chemical and waste pollution of our national water sources – pollution that affects tap water in every home in the country.

As agricultural production has grown, so has the power of one particular body, the National Farmers' Union (NFU), which occupies a unique position in British political life. The power of its lobby is respected and feared throughout Whitehall. The Ministry of Agriculture has traditionally seen its role as the protector of the farming interest. No other industry has an entire government ministry dedicated to nurturing and protecting it. Critics say that it protects the farmers at the expense of the general public, who must buy their overpriced produce and drink water contaminated by their farming practices.

Sir Richard Body, a former Conservative chairman of the House of Commons Agriculture Select Committee, has calculated that the farmers have managed to squeeze no fewer than forty different kinds of state aid out of the government. They have negotiated subsidies both for producing food and for not producing food. They have been paid millions of pounds to drain land for ploughing and to refrain from draining land for ploughing. There have been grants, subsidies and tax privileges. Whichever way the wind blows, the big farmers never seem to lose out. Sir Richard has first-hand experience of the political influence of the farming lobby: 'To be a chairman or vice-chairman of one of these NFU committees is to have instant access to the Ministry,' he wrote in the *Independent* in January 1989.

If anyone doubts the formidable power of the farmers, the great Edwina Currie egg row of 1988–9 should serve as an object lesson in the use of political muscle. Readers may have differing opinions about Mrs Currie's politics, but the way she was bullied out of office shocked many health and environmental activists. The Royal College of Nursing and the President of the Faculty of Community Medicine voiced their concern that a junior minister could lose her job for speaking out against the farming interest. The *Sunday Times* described certain Tory backbenchers as the 'hired guns' of the NFU.

Dr David Player, the former Director General of the Health Education Council (HEC), believes that the farming lobby forced him too out of public life for criticizing the food, tobacco and alcohol lobbies. He says that Mrs Currie's resignation 'raises serious issues of how far health ministers can warn the public about health issues that cut across the interests of the food lobby. When I was there at the HEC and raised these issues the Ministry of Agriculture was in there like a ton of bricks, acting virtually as a lobby for the NFU.' An editorial in the *Independent* concluded, 'The Ministry of Agriculture has become an anachronistic embarrassment.'

When we investigated agricultural pollution of the water environment we found many similar political themes: negligible action against farmers who grossly pollute their local environment, and a stubborn unwillingness to take public-health measures that might cut into farm profits, even when such proposals are backed by EEC law. In the words of Sir Richard Body, when his committee investigated pesticides and their effects on human health, 'It found the attitude of government officials quite different from that of their counterparts in the US and Canada. The latter acted on the assumption that as pesticides kill pests, they might damage humans too, and strict control was thus needed . . . The best that can be said for the Ministry of Agriculture is that its role in food safety is incompatible with its enthusiasm for increased food production.'

The root of the problem is that the Ministry currently looks after the interests of both farmers and consumers. Sir Richard Body has argued for a new and separate Department of Food and Health, which would work to prevent the contamination of food and drinking water. Successive health alerts over eggs, cheese, poultry and cook-chill products make this conclusion ever more convincing. The interests of consumer safety and of farmers' profits would then be served by different bodies.

You might expect farmers to be keen on protecting the environment. Working on the land, they are its natural guardians. But although some do their best to minimize pollution, others seem less than concerned. Tony Davies, a former director of Anglian Water, told us that during his time at the water authority the farming community did not seem particularly interested in protecting water supplies. 'I think they're more concerned about enhancing their crop production, or have been until recently.' He mentioned a tendency among farmers to see the land as their own property for them to deal with as they wished. 'The farming fraternity must realize that the land may be theirs but the underground water is not.'

Not all farmers are tarred with the same brush, and some are very conservation-minded. But the NFU is dominated by the big guns – the grain barons who have time to spend in London, bending the ears of ministers. It is they who have consistently pressed for profitability and increased production. And if they are finally forced to adopt measures to safeguard the environment, they want compensation.

It is on compensation that plans to prevent agricultural water pollution have so far foundered. The best way to protect water supplies from contamination by agricultural chemicals is to stop chemicals from being used in that area – in other words, to set up water-protection zones. These have been tried in West Germany, Italy and Switzerland and have proved very effective. The British government has expressed its intention of setting up similar zones here, but the farmers want compensation for not polluting.

Professor Norman Moore, formerly of the Nature Conservancy Council, believes that 'Modern farming is very destructive of wildlife. It is transforming grasslands and having a colossal effect on insects, plants and animals.' Yet he doesn't lay the blame entirely at the farmers' door: 'The farmers are only acting within the framework provided by government. We as a nation have supported them. After the war it was necessary to increase production, but subsequent overproduction has had a huge effect. Conservation has not been a priority with successive governments.'

Robin Grove-White at the Centre for Environmental Technology told us, 'My main impression is of a quite deliberate official myopia about the side-effects of agricultural intensification throughout the late 1960s and early 1970s. No one looked seriously at the long-term implications, both biological and cultural.'

The farming lobby is not acting alone. Other groups have considerable interests in feeding modern agriculture's chemical addiction: ICI, Rhône-Poulenc, Shell, Shearing and the other multinational companies that control the pesticides market. They too have a powerful lobby. The fertilizer manufacturers are also busy pressing the government. Finally there are the consumers, who have nobody to represent their interests effectively except for a few voluntary-aided pressure groups. Even the water authorities cannot compete with the influence of the farmers and the chemists. Overall it is not surprising that so little has been done. Privately many water-authority officials believe that rural pollution is running out of control but feel that their hands are tied. Speaking on *World in Action*, Richard White from the Water Authorities Association commented: 'It's not possible to make progress without a lead from central government because it's not for water authorities to tell farmers what they should do. This has to be led by central government and it has to be a concerted effort.'

As we examine farm pollution in the following sections, time and again we come back to politics. Without the political will to confront the polluters there is little chance of significant improvement. The government sets the tone and makes the rules: at the moment the rules seem to invite farmers to damage our rivers and to threaten the purity of our drinking water.

The toxic cocktail: pesticides in drinking water

Drinking water all over the country is subject to extensive and illegal contamination by an unstable cocktail of highly toxic pesticides and herbicides. We consume them only in small doses, but we know next to nothing about the long-term effects of what we are drinking. These chemicals are, after all, designed to kill.

It is an alarming thought, though apparently not alarming enough to prompt government action. Britain is failing to comply with the EEC drinking-water directive that sets strict limits on pesticide contamination. Pesticides are frequently found in quantities far above the permissible levels. Politicians often exhort us to obey the law. In this case, with public health at stake, the British government itself has decided to break the law and is instructing the water industry to do likewise.

Pesticides and herbicides reach our drinking water from a variety of sources. About half of the pollution is the result of modern farming practice. The international chemical industry, expanding alongside the 'industrial' agriculture it services, produces millions of tonnes of powerful agro-chemicals every year. Poisonous chemicals also seep into our water supplies from industry, from large-scale weed-killing programmes carried out by local councils and from the extensive spraying of railway lines by British Rail.

Now, let's be honest: we don't like creepy-crawlies. We don't like them in our food, on ourselves, in our houses or where we work. Nor do we like weeds sprouting through pavements or taking over cabbage patches. So we indulge in chemical warfare, spreading pesticides and herbicides on our crops and in our gardens. We place a premium on food that looks nice and clean. Companies that supply those up-market ready-made salads to the big supermarket chains know that if a customer finds so much as half a caterpillar in the cauliflower sprigs they run the risk of losing a valuable contract. Consequently some market-garden produce is sprayed and dusted far beyond any reasonable requirement to keep away harmful pests. These chemicals may make our food look appealing, and they certainly boost farmers' profits, but they are still a potential threat to human health.

The pesticide industry has grown dramatically in the last few decades. Worldwide sales are over £15 billion a year. It is estimated that in this country alone 4.5 billion litres of pesticide spray are used on crops every year.[1] Already dissolved into water for easy application, these pesticides and herbicides are in an ideal state to percolate down into the water system and work their way inexorably towards our kitchen taps.

The extent of our ignorance about pesticides is chilling. It is difficult to believe that we allow the widespread application of dangerous chemicals about which so little is known. Our capacity to invent, manufacture and market these toxic products seems to outstrip by far our interest in testing, regulating and monitoring them. Farmers do not have to tell the water authorities what they are spraying; neither do local councils or

British Rail. We do not know what percentage of a given application reaches drinking-water sources, or how long it remains there. We do not know the effects of long-term exposure to many of these chemicals individually, or the results of exposure to mixtures of them. And we do not know with any certainty which chemicals are likely to pollute drinking water in the first place because tests for some of them simply do not exist. It is bad enough when a load of pesticide or herbicide is spilled near a river. The water authority has to act quickly to shut down any water-intake points to make sure none gets into the supply. But here we are concerned with the steady drip of poisons into the rivers and groundwater from which we get our drinking-water supplies.

Despite serious monitoring problems, it is possible to estimate the scale of pesticide pollution of our drinking water. In 1988 Friends of the Earth analysed the available records of water authorities and water companies for the period July 1985 to June 1987. The Anglian region, the most intensively farmed area in the country, was found to have the worst record for pesticide contamination of drinking water. No fewer than eleven pesticides were detected in quantities over the EEC limit, and the region's drinking water contained the highest overall concentration of pesticides and herbicides. Runner-up was the Severn Trent area. Seven pesticides had broken the EEC limit here, including the powerful herbicide Bromoxynil, which has recently been banned for use in domestic gardens and for any use involving hand-held applicators. Bromoxynil was measured in Severn Trent surface-water sources at up to fourteen times the legal limit for drinking water. It would appear that while people are not allowed to touch it, it is all right for them to drink it. In the north-west, following one farm-pollution incident, Atrazine, a popular 'total weedkiller', was detected in surface water at ten times the EEC limit. Atrazine has produced tumours when tested on animals and is described as 'moderately toxic to humans via the oral route'. Illegal concentrations of this pesticide were also detected in the Wessex region, along with Simazine and Propazine. A sample in Yorkshire was found to contain Dieldrin, a powerful insecticide rated 'extremely hazardous' by the World Health Organization, at levels above the EEC limit. (Dieldrin is one of a family of powerful chemicals called the 'drins', which have been used as a dust on potatoes, as a bulb dip for narcissus plants and as a wood preserver. One nanogram of Dieldrin in a litre of water makes for a concentration of just one part per trillion. This sounds negligible, but, according to the water industry's own Water Research Council, 'sub-lethal effects have been observed' in some species at this level. These sub-lethal effects include skeletal deformations in fish and bio-chemical abnormalities in many organisms. In larger doses the chemical causes birth defects and cancer in experimental animals and is highly toxic to birds, fish and mammals. Dieldrin is known to be extremely persistent in the environment, and many rivers are still believed to be polluted with it. Not surprisingly, environmentalists have been campaigning for years to have the 'drins' banned.)

Friends of the Earth believe that their figures for illegal pesticide contamination represent a gross underestimate of the true situation. The Association of Public Analysts recently found that a third of tap-water samples contained measurable traces of pesticides. Atrazine, widely used on railway embankments and road sides, has been found in groundwater throughout Britain for many years, and the British Geological Survey has found persistent herbicides in East Anglian groundwater at concentrations ranging from two to twenty times the legal limit. Whenever government spokespeople or the water authorities attempt to reassure the public about the amount of pesticides in drinking water they tell us that such things are present only in 'very small quantities'. This is true. It is hard to imagine a quantity smaller than a nanogram, for instance. (A nanogram is only one thousand millionth of a gram. And a gram, to most of us, is pretty small to start with.) Yet some chemicals, such as Dieldrin, are dangerous even at levels that can barely be measured. The chemical industry itself is now worried about its products finding their way into people's drinking water. B. G. Johen of the Environmental Sciences Group of ICI has called it 'one of the most important issues facing agriculture, the public and the agricultural chemicals industry today'.

The most persistent pesticides remain in the environment for years. Reg Green at the International Confederation of Free Trade Unions in Brussels says, 'They're designed to last a long time, to the extent that you'd have trouble finding a single mother in the UK whose milk didn't contain traces of the more ubiquitous compounds, such as DDT, which is now banned.' The Department of the Environment provides a table of thirty-two common pesticides. Of these there is no information available on the persistence of twenty-five. Twenty may, or are likely to, reach water. When pesticides are approved for use their persistence is usually expressed in terms of how long they survive in soil, but some live a good deal longer in water. The herbicide 2,4-D, commonly used by local councils, has a lifespan in soil of only a few days, but it survives in water for over six months.

Another reason why we cannot assess accurately the potential health hazard of pesticides in drinking water is that most supplies are not tested routinely for low levels of many common pesticides. Tests are simply not available. According to Andrew Lees of Friends of the Earth, 'We have about 350 pesticide active ingredients approved for use in this country. We have routine analytical capability for only fifty of them. In consequence the information we have so far about the nature and the extent of the contamination is a gross underestimate because in practice it has not been properly investigated.' The proportion of pesticides that are detected has been variously estimated at between 12 and 40 per cent of what is really there. We are simply unaware of the presence of many toxic compounds.

Worrying too is the tendency of pesticides to react with each other and with other chemicals already in the water. We know very little about the resulting cocktail, though it may well be more dangerous than the sum of its parts. The Water Research Council has said, 'Our knowledge of the toxicology of mixtures is limited.' It has also mentioned a further complication: the effect of disinfection with chlorine, which 'may convert the pesticide into other chemicals with different toxicological properties'. It is a mathematical impossibility to work out, and test, all of the potential permutations – a good reason for working towards the eradication of all pesticides from drinking water.

Certainly such chemicals, once absorbed, are extremely hard to get rid of. Most are 'bio-accumulative', building up in the tissue of living organisms and then becoming ever more concentrated the higher up the food chain they progress. In 1986 Dieldrin pollution in the Avon near Coventry led to the death of a number of herons. The birds had been feeding on eels, and the eels had acted rather like 'pollution mops', absorbing Dieldrin from the worms on which they were feeding. In 1988 eels at thirty-seven of the sixty-two British sampling sites contained dangerous levels of Dieldrin, forcing the Ministry of Agriculture to issue a warning to people who regularly eat eels. One eel fished out of the Leeds–Liverpool canal was found to contain Dieldrin at over forty times the Department of Health's recommended maximum amount. Eels from the Thames at Richmond contained six times the recommended maximum amount of Dieldrin.

No one can say for sure just what harm is done to us by long-term exposure to pesticides in our water and our diet. We know what will happen to people if they drink a bottle of weedkiller: they will become very ill and may die. We don't know what will happen to people who drink small quantities of that same weedkiller in daily cups of coffee. We do know that some of these chemicals are very dangerous. Some cause cancer or reproductive problems such as miscarriage or birth defects in laboratory animals; some even damage the genetic material of cells so that defects are passed on to succeeding generations.

In the past doctors studying the effects of trace chemicals have been accused of quackery by their more traditional colleagues, but mainstream doctors are now taking the medical effects of our toxic environment more seriously, and the British Medical Association has set up a committee to investigate the effects of low doses of pesticide. Dr Gabriel Scally, a community physician in Belfast, explained: 'Doctors are getting more interested in the quality of drinking water. The effects of a low level of pesticides appear to be poorly researched. But a recent American report seems to suggest that they could cause cancer ... We know the effects on animals: birds of prey, for instance, are declining because of pesticides. And we know the effects of large doses: a high dose of Paraquat will cause death through renal failure. Most pesticides affect the liver or kidneys because these have the job of excreting them. Some pesticides cause neurological damage – i.e. loss of function, sensory loss and loss of movement.' The British Geological Survey is another respected institution that is taking this problem seriously. In 1987 it concluded that pesticides in drinking water 'represent a serious health hazard, since they are all, to a greater or lesser degree, chemically tailored to be toxic and persistent' and many of them 'break down into toxic derivatives'. As usual the groups potentially most at risk are those who drink most water in relation to their body weight: babies and young children.

One theory is that repeated exposure to hazardous chemicals like Dieldrin may cause cancer. At least one in five of us can expect to die from cancer,[2] whereas at the turn of the century the figure was one in twenty-two. Of course, part of the reason for this increase in deaths from cancer is that people live a good deal longer and do not now succumb to diseases such as tuberculosis. Cancer, therefore, claims a larger percentage of total deaths. But this doesn't account for all the increase.

Many cancers are certainly triggered by environmental factors. The London Food Commission (LFC) has been studying pesticides in food and drinking water for several years. Peter Snell of the LFC believes that 'It's fairly safe to assume that some cancer deaths each year have been triggered by low-level pesticide exposure.' He believes there can be no safe lower limit for chemicals that cause cancer. Andrew Lees of Friends of the Earth comments, 'We're dealing with substances many of which are certainly animal carcinogens and therefore presumptive human carcinogens. The question is: what increased incidence of cancer is acceptable to the public? The public are never asked to decide about that. They're always told that drinking water is absolutely safe.'

The LFC has calculated that forty-nine pesticides have been linked with cancer, thirty-one with birth defects and eighty-nine with allergy and skin irritation. One study suggests that in the course of a single generation the number of cases of eczema has increased five times and the number of cases of asthma has increased three times. Both of these diseases are strongly linked with an allergic reaction to environmental pollutants. In addition, the LFC says, 'At least sixty-one commonly used pesticides, permitted for use on foods, have been implicated as mutagens or suspect mutagens . . . There are clear grounds for caution in the use of all pesticides on foods once they have been implicated as mutagenic agents.' (This means that they have been shown to damage the genetic material of cells, causing mutations in the cells that are passed on to every subsequent generation.)

There is also concern about new diseases – for example, myalgic encephalomyelitis (ME). The cause of this debilitating disease is not known, but the ME Action Campaign says that it is 'probably the result of a malfunction of the immune system. It is believed that environmental factors are responsible. It is now known that pesticide residues in foodstuffs do damage the immune system and expose the person to new and dangerous illnesses from viral infections. Everyone could be at risk.' The campaign organizers say that there may be as many as 100,000 people in Britain currently suffering from some form of ME.

Of course, pesticides and herbicides have to be tested for safety before they can be approved for use. Some tests have been shocking. In his book *Gluttons for Punishment* James Erlichman tells a story about the Swiss company Ciba-Geigy, which chose to test one unproven pesticide by spraying it on a group of specially recruited Egyptian schoolchildren and analysing their urine to see if any got through.[3] Companies also send their products to industrial testing laboratories. But these have not always been reliable in the past. One of the most scandalous aspects of the pesticide story is the extent to which safety approvals have been based on spurious and fraudulent test results. One company in particular was less than scrupulous in carrying out safety tests for pesticides. This company was Industrial

Bio-Test (IBT) of Illinois, whose testing methods were un-orthodox, to say the least. Tests were faked; dead animals were replaced by live ones during tests; and when experimental mice escaped from their cages and got mixed up together, data were simply made up. It was on evidence such as this that many chemicals were declared safe for use. Despite its appalling sloppiness, IBT was no tinpot company. Andrew Lees says, 'Industrial Bio-Test was then the world's largest toxicological testing company. Cyhexatin, for instance, relied in part on IBT data. When cyhexatin was re-tested by today's standards it turned out to cause birth defects and was banned. When dinoseb was re-tested by today's standards it turned out to cause birth defects and was banned.'

It is reassuring to know that some of the dangerous chemicals that relied on suspect testing have now been proscribed. But not all pesticides have been re-tested. There is a rolling pro-gramme to carry out new safety tests on all chemicals currently in use, but because there are so many of them this programme will take twenty years to complete. Meanwhile they are still being spread on the ground. Andrew Lees calls this 'scandal-ous'. Dr Alastair Hay, of the Department of Chemistry at Leeds University, says, 'They promised a rolling programme, but it is rolling much too slowly.'

Speaking for water-industry scientists, Dr R. Packham of the Water Research Council told a House of Commons Select Committee in 1986, 'We do not have comprehensive informa-tion on pesticides in drinking water as such, and that lack of information is something worrying.' In the light of all this ignorance, surely there is a strong case for at least sticking to the present EEC regulations? But we don't.

Aware of the risk that poisonous chemicals would pollute the water supply, the EEC was keen to set limits. But it had a problem. There are about 300 pesticides and herbicides in use, and some are more toxic than others. To set a limit for each would be very cumbersome. So instead the Commissioner set a maximum admissible concentration (MAC) for total pesticides and related products of 0.5 micrograms per litre (μg/l), with a limit of 0.1 μg/l for any one individual pesticide.

The Water Research Council has not greeted these limits with much enthusiasm. In evidence to a House of Commons Agriculture Committee it said, 'The figures are not based on toxicological data, and the derivation is not clear. Many authorities consider that the MAC for individual pesticides is too high for some and too low for others.' It concluded that the single limit 'does not provide a sensible basis for assessing drinking-water quality, nor does it provide an adequate level of consumer protection'.

Because it does not consider the EEC limits to be sensible, the government has chosen to ignore them, much to the fury of Friends of the Earth. Andrew Lees says, 'In August 1987 the Department of the Environment wrote to water authorities and water companies about the pesticides parameter in the drinking-water directive. That advice, which is still the government's current advice, in effect asks them to ignore the EEC limit. It does not ask them to report all breaches of the limit to the government.' David Wheeler, Research Fellow at the Robens Institute of Industrial and Environmental Health and Safety at Surrey University, says that this will continue after privatization: 'There will still be a considerable degree of flexibility for the water industry in deciding which pesticides should be monitored.'

The EEC limits for pesticides came into force in July 1985. Since then Friends of the Earth has collected evidence of breaches of them. It has found that in the two years to June 1987 the limit for a single pesticide was exceeded in 298 water sources and the limit for the total pesticides in water breached on seventy-six occasions. If water authorities were able to carry out more frequent and more sophisticated monitoring, and if sufficient tests were available for all the chemicals in water, the problem would be seen to be much worse.

In 1987 the EEC said that it would initiate formal proceedings against the UK government for flouting the law in this way. In the words of Stanley Clinton-Davis, the EEC Environment Commissioner, 'It is a disgrace that member states should fail to respect the laws which they have themselves adopted. Water quality is a matter of wide public concern, and we have an obligation to see that the law is respected.'

The government may say that it wishes standards to be based on 'sound scientific judgement'. Sceptics feel that the government is really trying to make things easy for itself. For instance, in 1986 the British government set its own guideline values for various pesticides. Several of these were far above the EEC limits and even above World Health Organization (WHO) guidelines. In the case of Atrazine the EEC limit is 0.1 μg/l; the WHO recommend 2 μg/l; the UK government plumped for 30 μg/l. Then there are the 'drins'. Britain is the only EEC member state that still permits their use. Despite a mountain of scientific evidence about the environmental hazards posed by this class of toxic-persistent organochlorine pesticides, the government proposes to permit the continued use of Aldrin in agriculture and horticulture until 1993. So much for sound scientific judgement.

The fact is that EEC limits for pesticides in drinking water were set very low to encourage governments to remove pesticides from public drinking water altogether. Most people would surely agree with this objective. In the light of what we know about their toxicity, and what we do not know about their long-term 'cocktail' effects, it seems only sensible to work towards excluding pesticides from our drinking water. Any government that wishes to create a safer and less toxic environment for its citizens can do nothing less.

Maybe we should ask ourselves why we wage chemical warfare on our environment in the first place. Wouldn't wild flowers look just as good on grass verges and railway embankments as grass alone? And do we need so many chemicals on crops? Organic farmers depend not on pesticides to produce their harvest but on pest predators, creatures that are also, incidentally, killed off by the application of pesticides. It surely cannot be a viable long-term policy to rely on a form of agriculture that pollutes soil and water with ever-increasing quantities of poison. If some pesticides are essential if we are to feed ourselves, every effort must be made to prevent them from reaching our drinking water. Obeying the current law would be a good start.

Rivers of waste: farm-pollution incidents

Like any industry, farming produces waste – in particular, millions of litres of animal urine and excrement. If mishandled, such waste can do tremendous damage to the rural water environment. The concentrated animal waste in farm slurry is between eighty and a hundred times more polluting than untreated human sewage. Silage-making can also create problems. The liquor that is produced can be 200 times more polluting than human waste.[4] Yet, perhaps because we view this waste as somehow 'natural', the fines for pollution are derisory: most are under £500. We heard of one farmer who built himself a large slurry lagoon with Ministry of Agriculture grants and was responsible for serious pollution of the Trent canal for several years. He was fined £150.

Since 1979 water-pollution incidents involving farm waste have increased by 150 per cent.[5] Intensively reared cattle and pigs are the major source. Waste from piggeries and cattle sheds should be stored for later use as fertilizer or for gradual disposal, as agreed with the local water authority. Running water can break down and render harmless a certain amount of waste, but if a great quantity suddenly finds its way into a small river or stream, the consequences can be extreme: the river's capacity to absorb the waste is overwhelmed; bacteria thrive; oxygen levels plummet; and aquatic life is extinguished.

Modern intensive farming can generate staggering quantities of waste. One Lincolnshire farmer ran what local people called a 'concentration camp for cattle'. The unfortunate animals produced an estimated 67,500 litres of urine per day. Five kilometres of chalkstream were affected by effluent from the farm. The farmer was fined £1,000 with £700 costs. The Severn–Trent water authority reports that in 1985 the rupture of a tank allowed 225,000 litres of pig slurry to drain into a river. Corrosion was responsible, caused by damage to the tank ten years before. The inspectors said that the need for repairs would have been apparent long before the rupture occurred. The farmer was fined £1,650.

The problem is nationwide. Over 1,000 homes in remote west Wales were ordered by loudspeaker vans to boil their drinking water in January 1989. Farm slurry had polluted a borehole. In the Thames Water Authority area in 1987 an incident de-oxygenated the Derry Brook from its source to the confluence with the Thames. In Northumberland during the same year 4,000 trout died after a large discharge of slurry into a river. After 450,000 litres of slurry polluted a river in the South West Water Authority area, killing many fish, the farmer responsible was fined just £500 plus £100 costs. The North West Water Authority reports: 'In 1986 some 47.7 kilometres of classified water courses were downgraded solely as a consequence of farm wastes.' Severn Trent Water Authority says that 131 kilometres of river deteriorated in 1986–7, mainly because of repeated minor agricultural pollution incidents.

Such reports evoke an image of a countryside not so much flowing with milk and honey as overflowing with silage and pig slurry. Doubtless a majority of farmers do respect their land and the water flowing through it, but an unscrupulous minority sees a stream as a convenient sewer. Most get away with it or else face minimal fines, running rings around the laws meant to protect our national water resources. Since 1980 903 kilometres of rivers in England and Wales have deteriorated in quality. According to Surrey University's Robens Institute, this 'reflects critically on the inability of water authorities to exert proper regulatory controls on industry and agriculture. This has implications for drinking-water quality.' A report from the Department of the Environment cites problems in such rural havens as the river Cherwell near Banbury, the Cut near Windsor, the Thame near Aylesbury, the Wellow near Bath and the Parrett in Somerset. In Devon the once beautiful river Torridge, the setting for *Tarka the Otter*, is now seriously polluted, the result, local campaigners believe, of repeated pollution by untreated farm waste. In an unusually strong statement for a water authority, Welsh Water reported recently that 1987 'represented by far the worst year ever as far as farm pollution is concerned'. In addition to reported incidents, 'Studies presently being undertaken by Welsh Water scientists

are revealing chronic cases of farm pollution not being reported
to the authority ... Farming is now well into a phase where it
is being required to retain large volumes of highly polluting
liquid in tanks and lagoons.'

The Water Authorities Association blames a minority of
farmers who dump waste in an attempt to save money: 'Although most farmers do spend considerable sums of money to
prevent discharges, the cost of waste containment is undoubtedly a factor for the 1 per cent of all farmers who are
responsible for pollution incidents.'

Farm-waste pollution poisons rivers, but humans do not
always escape. In February 1989 there was a worrying outbreak
of diarrhoea in Oxfordshire and Wiltshire. The organism
cryptosporidia, normally found in farm animals, infected hundreds of consumers in the Oxford and Swindon areas. A
water-treatment plant that supplies these areas was found to be
contaminated with cryptosporidia – probably as a result of
farm slurries reaching the public water supply. Consumers
were warned to boil all water intended for children under
two years old. It emerged that many water-treatment works
may not be equipped to remove the organism and may need
modification.

Water authorities do take the problem seriously, and much
effort goes into tracking down offending farmers and land-
owners. The number of successful court actions has risen
sharply in recent years. However, inspectors complain bitterly
about the level of fines. They can spend months tracking down
the source of a particularly damaging pollution incident, only to
see the farmer responsible receive a minimal fine at the hands
of rural magistrates. In some cases fines have been as low as
£25. In the South West Water Authority area the average fine
for twenty-two cases was £141. Yet the total cost to the water
authority of clearing up after an incident can be several
thousand pounds.

With fines this low, there is little incentive for persistent
offenders to mend their ways. Jim Wild, from Severn Trent
Water Authority, says: 'Farmers generally regard themselves as
the guardians of the environment and try to take care of it. But

a small residual group really doesn't seem to care. The fines imposed are so meagre they tend to think: Why should I bother?' It is not difficult to see why inspectors sometimes privately despair. One farmer in the Severn Trent area was recently fined £500. It was his third pollution offence in three years, but the farm keeps changing its company name, so each case had to be considered as a first offence. Jim Wild also tells the story of one of the worst incidents he has witnessed. Untreated human sewage has a biological oxygen demand (BOD) level – a measure of pollution's capacity to de-oxygenate water – of about 250 milligrams per litre (mg/l). In 1987 silage liquor with a BOD of 43,000 mg/l polluted a reservoir in Welshpool. Jim Wild laconically calls this 'pretty thick'. It completely de-oxygenated a reservoir with a capacity of 40.5 million litres, and the water authority spent £4,000 on aeration equipment to prevent a public health hazard. The man responsible for the pollution was fined £300.

The state of the river Torridge is a particularly sad example of what can happen to a river in an area of modern intensive farming. The amount of farm waste reaching the river system has severely damaged the river's ability to support wildlife. The otters that inspired *Tarka the Otter* have gone, as have many of the fish that once made the Torridge a famous salmon stream. South West Water reported in 1986 that 'in the last ten years large fish mortalities have been caused by discharges from agricultural sources and traders' and describes the pollution effects of a dairy herd of fifty-three cows, the average for Devon. Making silage to feed such a herd through the winter produces 145,000 litres of silage effluent, to be disposed of at the rate of 19,000 litres per day. 'The potential pollution load of this effluent is equivalent to that of a community of 10,800 inhabitants,' says the water authority. It has been estimated that the entire agricultural waste-handling and disposal problem in the river Torridge catchment area is equivalent to dealing with the sewage of 600,000 people.

Little seems to change. Year in, year out, water authority reports contain the same calls for more urgency, for higher fines, for the introduction of publicity campaigns and for tougher measures to tackle the problem of farm waste disposal. In 1988 a government minister, John Gummer, pointed out that 'The polluting farmer damages his neighbours as well as the water course. They suffer from his failures, and he undoes all the good which their proper management of farm waste has achieved. Nineteen eighty-eight must be the year when the farming community gets really tough with pollution.' So far there is no evidence that it was.

On tap from the chemical farm: nitrates in drinking water

Nitrate is the mainstay of life down on the chemical farm, and the figures are impressive. Britain's consumption of nitrate fertilizer increased from 60,000 tonnes a year in the late thirties to just below 200,000 tonnes by the mid-forties and then leapt to a 1985 figure of 1,580,000 tonnes a year.[6] This enormously increased quantity of fertilizer is also used much more intensively; almost twice as much is applied per hectare as was the case even fifteen years ago. In all, Britain's farmers spend some £600 million a year on nitrate fertilizer.

Stuart Crocker of the Soil Association tries to promote organic farming, a form of agriculture that does not rely on the extensive use of chemicals. Organic farmers like Stuart are introducing modern crop rotations and methods of growing crops that respect and replenish the soil. 'We aim for a living soil,' he contends, 'in contrast to the inert soil medium regarded as necessary by agribusiness.' Organic farmers work a few smallholdings; thousands of hectares are given over to hedgerow-less 'megafarms'. Already 56 per cent of agricultural production comes from just 11 per cent of farms.[7] In January 1989 the Agriculture Minister, John MacGregor, welcomed this trend, saying that smaller farms are usually inefficient and would continue to be squeezed out. The rise of the arable monoculture seems inexorable, a form of industrial farming that depends on smothering the soil in nitrate.

Some of this nitrate seeps into underground watercourses and, in time, into the tap water of millions of people. In fact, the leaching of nitrates into public drinking water has given the government and the water industry one of their biggest headaches in the run-up to privatization. It has already provoked a furious row with the EEC, in which the government has been accused of fiddling the figures in an attempt to escape European health guidelines. These EEC guidelines are now to be more closely adhered to, and the Department of the Environment has ruled that the new, private, water companies must do what the government itself has avoided doing: obey the rules about nitrate pollution of drinking water. But it seems likely that the substantial costs of meeting the European limit will fall not on those responsible for the original pollution but on the consumer, through sharply increased water charges. Thus the millions of people who today receive tap water that breaks the European limit for nitrate pollution look likely to be the ones who pay for its removal.

Nitrate leaches into the water-table throughout the year, but it is a particular problem in the autumn and winter, when plants absorb less fertilizer. The nitrate seeps down through the soil until it reaches an impermeable layer, such as clay, but then it doesn't just stay where it is. It begins to move sideways, frequently finding its way to underground reservoirs and water courses. One of the problems in tackling nitrate pollution is that this leaching process takes many years to complete. Groundwater levels of nitrate are rising at the moment and would continue to rise even if all fertilizers were banned tomorrow. Nitrate that was applied to the soil five or maybe ten years ago is only now seeping into our water supplies. So we are dealing today with the nitrate levels of the early 1980s. As more nitrate is applied we store up even more trouble for the future. The government's own Nitrate Co-ordination Group said in 1986, 'The vast majority of groundwater sources display an overall rising trend in nitrate levels. It is likely that there will be a continuing and slow rise in groundwater nitrate concentrations in most unconfined aquifers.' There have been predictions that if current farming practices continue unchecked, the concentrations of nitrate in some groundwater in intensively farmed arable areas could be double or treble the 'safe' level permitted by the EEC.

Where nitrate runs off into rivers the damage it causes is obvious. The fertilizer encourages luxuriant plant growth, which, as it decays, takes up much of the available oxygen in the water, leaving fish to suffocate. A Royal Society report in 1984 said that in some rivers levels of nitrate had quadrupled in the previous twenty years. When it reaches the sea nitrate promotes the formation of vast colonies of algae, threatening the oxygen supply of marine life.

In May 1988 massive blooms of algae swept around the coasts of Scandinavia, suffocating fish and other sea creatures. One Danish fish farmer reported that his entire stock of salmon had been wiped out. At one stage a single concentrated slick of fertilizer-enriched algae, 10–30 metres deep and nearly 10 kilometres wide, snaked around the Scandinavian coast. Millions of sea fish are thought to have died. This was the third such incident in eight successive years, and it left Scandinavian fishermen complaining bitterly about the amount of nitrate that was finding its way into the sea. Some spoke of a 'marine Chernobyl'. The Norwegian government alone reported that the incident had cost it over £120 million. Closer to home, scientists believe that conditions in the Wash are now suitable for a deadly algae bloom that would afflict the British coast. Denmark has already taken steps to control the use of nitrate fertilizer, but most of the nitrate in the North Sea is washed out of other countries, including Britain – 1.5 million tonnes of it every year.

In addition to the clear damage to the environment there are also serious concerns about a possible threat to human health. Bacteria in the mouth and stomach convert nitrate to a chemical called nitrite. This combines with haemoglobin in human red blood cells to form methaemoglobin. As a result oxygen uptake in the lungs is reduced. This is a particular problem in tiny babies, who can even turn blue from lack of oxygen, a condition known as cyanosis or blue-baby syndrome. Excess nitrate has also been linked with stomach cancer. It can react with substances in food to produce N-nitrosamines, chemicals that have been shown to cause cancer in thirty-nine animal species, including primates.

Taking account of the available scientific information, the EEC and the World Health Organization have set MACs for nitrate in public drinking water. These are levels that, international experts believe, should not be exceeded in order to protect the public health. The EEC has set a level of 50 milligrams per litre for nitrate and the World Health Organization one of 44.5 mg/l. According to the WHO, these values are 'concentrations which should not be exceeded over long periods of time because of the potential hazards of ingesting excessive amounts of these substances'. Friends of the Earth estimates that in Britain about 4 million people, mainly in East Anglia, Lincolnshire, Nottinghamshire and Staffordshire, receive water supplies that sometimes exceed the EEC limit of 50 mg/l.

In recent years the British government's attitude to these European limits has been simple. It has evaded them. It was clear to officials that in many parts of Britain nitrate levels were already frequently beyond 50 mg/l and actually closer to 80 or 100 mg/l. At this point the choices are clear: you begin a programme to clean up the water and cut down on the application of fertilizer, or you bend the rules. The government decided to bend the rules. Whitehall officials chose to interpret the 50 mg/l limit as a three-month average. They told the water authorities that samples would be allowed to reach 80 mg/l on occasion so long as the average figure remained below 50 mg/l. Thus if a region's water crept over the limit for only a few weeks every quarter, the overall performance might be judged to be within the limit and therefore acceptable. This elegant bureaucratic dodge amazed even connoisseurs of Whitehall's evasion of environmental standards. (It is not unlike saying to a drunk driver, 'You've been drunk only once this week, so on average you've been sober,' or telling shoplifters that since they steal only from one shop in every street, on average they have been law-abiding and will escape prosecution.)

When asked in 1987 why the British chose to re-interpret the European limits, Richard White of the Water Authorities Association offered the following explanation on *World in Action*: 'We go for 80 [mg/l], the rest of Europe goes for 50. There probably are cultural differences between Britain and Europe which lead us to question numbers that in parts of Europe . . . would be accepted.' The water authorities have to tread a delicate line here. All they can do is advise the government about the extent of the problem and then follow whatever decision is made about maximum permitted levels. But the 'cultural differences' between Britain and Europe to which Richard White referred may have something to do with the extensive influence of the farming community and the chemical industry in this country. Both can orchestrate a ferocious lobby when they feel their interests to be under threat.

When pressed about the evasion of nitrate-pollution controls, government and farming spokespeople often claim that there is no firm medical evidence that nitrate is a serious threat to human health. According to its publication 'The Nitrate in Water Debate', the NFU says that the EEC limit of 50 mg/l is 'too low for UK conditions. It was set arbitrarily and without any scientific base.' The NFU is also quick to point out that in this country there have been only fourteen cases of blue-baby syndrome in the last thirty-five years.

Environmentalists counter by pointing out that there have been cases of sub-clinical illness caused by oxygen starvation in the blood of small babies. ('Sub-clinical' means that the symptoms are not serious enough to warrant any urgent medical attention but that nevertheless the child is not developing normally.) A study in the USSR looked at a group of older children who drank water with a nitrate content of only half the EEC limit of 50 mg/l. The children were found to have elevated methaemoglobin in their blood and demonstrated slower reflexes than normal. Their central nervous systems were not developing as they should. A study in Israel found there to be a significant increase in methaemoglobin levels in infants even when their drinking water contained nitrate at levels permitted by the EEC.

A recent Department of Health memorandum points to a number of cases of blue-baby syndrome in which nitrate levels were in the range 50–100 mg/l. According to Andrew Lees of Friends of the Earth, the public-health officials who wrote the memorandum say that they are puzzled by these cases and offer a number of explanations. They conclude that, in the absence of any concrete explanation, it seems sensible to remain wary about water containing nitrate in the range 50–100 mg/l. Lees calls this approach 'highly commendable'.

There is also disagreement on the subject of stomach cancer. The NFU has commented, 'Research simply does not support the fear that high-nitrate water may be linked to stomach cancer', but the evidence was enough to persuade the major international health agencies that there was cause for concern. Studies in Britain do not support links between nitrate and cancer, but the WHO reports that studies in other countries do. And if the available evidence is enough to make the WHO and the EEC set safety limits for our drinking water, surely there is a strong case for observing them.

Andrew Lees says that the uncertainty in this area 'justifies making sure that water complies with the legal limit for nitrates. Stomach cancer, like many other cancers, can only be diagnosed many years after it's been triggered. There is what's called a latency period.' If there is a relationship, current patterns of stomach cancer relate to past exposures to nitrate, when the levels were far lower than they are now. If we want conclusive proof that today's higher nitrate levels are causing cancer, we will have to wait until a lot more people die. As Lees puts it, 'The farmers might well ask: "Where's the pile of bodies?" but our view is that by the time there's a pile of bodies, it's far too late.'

When there is room for doubt most people would choose to err on the side of caution where their long-term health is concerned. The last few decades have been littered with examples of products and chemicals that were thought to be dangerous but about which there was no definite, conclusive proof. It took years to prove to most people's satisfaction that tobacco was a killer; the same is true of asbestos and Thalidomide. It may well be that one day we will pronounce nitrate safe, but until that day comes it is dangerous to ignore the advice of international experts and, in effect, experiment on ordinary consumers of drinking water. Let the scientists decide in their laboratories what is, and what is not, dangerous. In the meantime we should stick by the rules and keep our water as clean and safe as possible.

The British government's decision to reinterpret the EEC nitrate limit in the early and mid-1980s provoked a bitter row. More animosity was to follow when some of the worst areas were simply 'derogated' – that is, allowed to break the limit for a certain period of time. Suppliers providing water to nearly 1 million people in the eastern counties and the Midlands were unable even to meet the government's relaxed standards, so they were excused. If the original 50 mg/l standard had been applied, as the EEC intended, the government would have had to admit that about 4 million people receive water that falls below EEC standards. The reason given for these derogations was that 'the nature and structure of the ground' in certain areas made it impossible for the water authorities to comply with directives about standards. In certain circumstances this argument is valid and is accepted by the EEC as a reason for not meeting drinking-water guidelines. But in the case of Britain nitrate pollution has less to do with the nature and structure of the ground than with the use of farm fertilizer.

In December 1986 Friends of the Earth formally reported the United Kingdom government to the EEC for refusing to obey European drinking-water law. It complained about the averaging of the figures and the exemptions, which Friends of the Earth said were illegal. After legal action was started by the EEC, the Secretary of State for the Environment backed down and admitted in Parliament that the EEC limit 'should relate to individual samples and not to averages over a period'. He also said, 'This is a technical point. It concerns the appearance of water supplied and does not have health implications.' Others disagreed. Following a further complaint in April 1988 the government withdrew certain derogations and now accepts that it should comply with the European limit of 50 mg/l of nitrate in drinking water. At the last count some 4 million people still receive water that sometimes has a nitrate concentration of over 50 mg/l.

In some high-nitrate areas it has already been necessary to set up bottling plants for babies and pregnant women. This has happened in the Anglian Water Authority area (although the bottling plants were not used) and in the Yorkshire Dales. In 1988 villages near Ripon, in Yorkshire, had bottled water provided for babies under six months because the local borehole was so badly contaminated with nitrates. Sister Egin, a local midwife in the village of Wath, said, 'Several villages were affected. The babies had to have water brought in for their first six months. We were told it was because of the high nitrate content, but there was no information on the technical bits.' Did anyone worry? 'We didn't make great store of it, really.' A few villagers, somewhat concerned about what the water might be doing to them, said they boiled it first. Unfortunately no one told them that boiling has no effect on the nitrate content. At worst it may concentrate it even further. A study from Iowa University in the USA concludes, 'Boiling and the resulting evaporation concentrates the nitrate in the remaining water and thereby increases the possibility of cyanosis.'

Reducing the level of nitrates in drinking water, and deciding who should pay for it, will require the judgement of a Solomon. One solution might be to increase the price of fertilizer to discourage farmers from using it, but the price increase would have to be dramatic before farmers were deterred. A better answer is probably water-protection zones, areas in which certain activities (for example, the ploughing of grassland or the use of nitrate fertilizer) are restricted. A few experimental water-protection zones have already been set up for nitrate. In Eastbourne nitrate concentration has been reduced from 60 mg/l to 35 mg/l. In compensation the farmers pay reduced rent to their local authority landlord. If such water-protection zones were introduced across the country, the measure could entail drastic changes in farming practice and possibly a loss of profits for some farmers. The NFU does not see why farmers should be made to suffer and is demanding compensation on their behalf. After all, they argue, it was Whitehall that encouraged them to boost arable farming in the first place. 'It would be quite unreasonable to penalize individual farmers for

co-operating with government policy or for what their pre-
decessors did many years ago', according to the NFU.

After reports of inter-departmental strife between the Department of the Environment and the Ministry of Agriculture,
water-protection zones were announced in November 1988. New
powers would allow ministers to ban nitrates, pesticides and
industrial solvents in some areas. There would be compensation
for the farmers and, possibly, a scheme to purify some heavily
contaminated water sources. As this book was written it
remained unclear just how extensive these zones would be. The
NFU said that press reports about a ban on fertilizers were
incorrect. Speaking on Radio 4's *The World at One*, the
Minister for Agriculture said restrictions would be a 'fall-back
position' in only a 'few limited cases'.

With the declared policy of privatization has come a promise
that the nitrate problem will finally be tackled. More money
will be spent on water treatment to remove nitrate and to
blend low-nitrate with high-nitrate water. In all it is estimated
that some £200 million will be needed in the next decade.
It looks likely that the consumer will have to foot the bill.
But is this fair? There is something called the Polluter Pays
Principle: those who cause pollution, and have benefited from
it, should have to pay to clear it up. In this case they would be
the farmers. A fertilizer tax of £7 a tonne, or 4 to 5 per cent,
would cover the likely expenditure on water treatment. Other
countries have also had to deal with this thorny question. In
some countries a tax on fertilizer has already been introduced
and water-protection zones established. But in Britain, according to Andrew Lees, 'The agricultural industry seems to be
arguing that the polluted, the water-rate payers, should pick up
the bill, while the polluters, the agricultural community, should
be compensated for not polluting. This makes a mockery of the
Polluter Pays Principle, which the Government claims to en-
dorse.'

The nitrate story is one that illustrates the prevailing attitude
in government towards environmental concerns. The EEC has
tried to introduce standards; Whitehall's response is to question
and evade them. When given a choice between the interests of

agriculture and worries about the state of the countryside and public health, Whitehall seems to bend over backwards to take the farmers' part, and, when finally brought to book, Whitehall decrees that the public will have to pay to clean up the mess.

2

THE POISON IN THE PIPES
Lead pollution of drinking water

We are a lead-damaged nation.
> *Dr Michael Moore, Glasgow University, 1988*

Lead makes kids thick.
> *Professor Derek Bryce-Smith, Reading University, 1988*

It's something that hasn't come up, and we haven't been teaching
mothers about that, I'm afraid.
> *Community midwife, water-lead problem area, 1987*

It is likely that people who buy this book are already concerned
about the environment, about eating healthy food and about
avoiding additives – they are people who probably take a great
deal of care in selecting food and drink for themselves and
their families. It may, therefore, come as a shock to discover
that almost half of readers with young families may well be
slowly poisoning their children every time they give them a
drink.[1] The poison is lead, and it comes out of the kitchen tap.

In the course of researching the *World in Action* report on
drinking-water pollution we came across the Malone family.
Stella and Kevin Malone lived with their two children in
Edinburgh. We were looking for high lead levels and were
testing tap water in Scotland. We had heard that the problem
was worse on the western side of the country and in Glasgow
but that in Edinburgh it was not so serious. Nevertheless we
discovered to our surprise, and to Stella Malone's horror, that
she was unwittingly feeding her baby son Kevin a dangerously
large dose of lead every time she gave him a bottle of baby milk
made up with tap water. Lead was coming out of the family's
taps in quantities way beyond those labelled dangerous by the
international scientific community.

Like any good parent, Stella Malone was careful to protect
her child's health when making up a feed: she sterilized the

bottle and boiled the tap water. But boiling has no effect on lead. Like many thousands of parents all around the country and on every day of the week, Stella Malone was feeding her child a potent dose of one of the most powerful brain poisons known to man.

This is not a well-publicized issue, and, like most people, we knew little about lead in drinking water when we began our research. What we discovered amazed us. We spoke to scientists who described Britain as a lead-damaged nation, yet we searched in vain for any evidence that our government has even begun to take the problem seriously. We found that a few simple precautions could reduce the risks, yet we came across no public-health information giving such advice or alerting people to the real danger they were in. We discovered young families drinking water with lead levels far above all international safety limits, yet even in the worst-affected areas we discovered that no official agency has troubled itself to warn parents about the tap water that is knocking 5, 10, maybe 15 per cent off the future intelligence levels of their children.

Lead is particularly damaging to the young, attacking the developing brains of foetuses in the womb and of young children, markedly reducing their intelligence. As Professor Derek Bryce-Smith of Reading University puts it, 'Lead makes kids thick.' In fact, the entire British population is to some extent 'lead-intoxicated', under-achieving, less intelligent than it could be, our minds impaired by lead. 'Lead is probably the most thoroughly documented of all known poisons. Even the Roman architect Vitruvius was aware of the danger of lead pipes,' says Bryce-Smith. It damages kidneys and raises blood pressure, but its most dramatic effects are on developing minds: it lessens intelligence, reduces memory and slows speech development. Professor Bryce-Smith also believes that lead impairs the mechanisms in the brain that control impulsive behaviour, making it a possible factor in delinquency, too.

Lead reaches the kitchen tap by means of water running through old lead pipes. There are thousands of miles of such pipework inside British homes, and lead pipes still carry water to houses all over the country. These pipes are crumbling fast, and more and more lead is dissolving into the drinking water the older they get. The softer the water, the more acidic it will be and the more lead it will dissolve.

Worst affected are people who live in older houses in acidic water areas. These include most of Scotland, the north of England, Wales and the West Country. Cities affected include Glasgow, Edinburgh, Birmingham, Liverpool, Manchester and Hull. Most houses built before 1964 have some lead pipework, and lead pipes were being fitted into some new homes for many years after that. It has been estimated that at least 10 million people live in areas at risk from lead in tap water – but such estimates were made at a time when scientists believed that small amounts of lead caused no harm. Now it is realized that there can be no 'safe' level of lead exposure, which means that many more people are at risk from a low-level, but still damaging, exposure to lead than was earlier thought. One estimate suggests that lead-polluted drinking water may be coming out of nearly half of all British taps.[2] Most of the studies, and the concern, about lead has come from the north and west of the country. This latest research means that homes right across southern England that have some lead in their plumbing must also now be classed as 'at risk'.

In fact, the most up-to-date scientific evidence has created something close to panic among concerned health researchers. In the last few years scientists have found that lead levels once considered safe are damaging children's memory, speech and learning. It now seems likely that hundreds of thousands of babies are being born throughout the country every year with enough lead already in their bodies to retard normal mental development.

Lead reaches us in several ways. Children who live near major roads are most at risk from car-exhaust fumes. Others may be exposed to lead in paint or plastics. But lead in drinking water is the most widespread form of lead pollution. It is odourless and tasteless and, most dangerous of all, it comes in a perfectly digestible form. Dissolved into drinking water and served up in a million glasses of orange squash or cups of tea, lead is what scientists term 'bio-available' – that is, in an ideal state to be absorbed into the human body.

Growing bodies absorb this 'bio-available' lead at a frightening rate. Because they are putting on weight so quickly, foetuses, babies and children take up lead from their diet at about five times the rate that adults do. However, according to Professor Bryce-Smith, the regulations governing lead levels have never taken this fact into account. Another expert agrees. Dr Michael Moore pioneered at Glasgow University research into the water-lead poisoning of children. He says, 'The international limits do not take into account the fact that children do absorb very much more lead in the early months of life.'

In Britain the dangers posed by lead in drinking water were first established by research in Glasgow and elsewhere in the 1970s. Dr Michael Moore was responsible for some of the most telling studies, which proved the long-suspected link between acidic water, lead pipes and mental retardation. The research showed that, among other problems, babies whose mothers drank water with a high lead content were twice as likely to be mentally retarded and were more likely to be stillborn. In the case of normal births only 7 per cent of placentae were found to contain high levels of lead; among stillbirths or those who died shortly after birth the figure was 61 per cent. In one experiment Dr Moore selected a group of adults and was able to find blood samples taken at their birth. On analysing these samples he found that adults who were classified as mentally retarded had been born with high levels of lead already in their bloodstream: Moore realized that the brains of these unfortunate people had been so damaged by lead exposure in the womb that they never stood a chance of developing normally. He soon discovered that the major source of this lead was tap water. The grim conclusion was that caring parents were, through no fault of their own, damaging their own children by simply drinking and serving what came out of the tap.

Dr Moore regularly found tap water in Glasgow containing lead at ten, fifteen or twenty times the safety limits of the time. He came across rural hamlets and farms with long runs of lead pipe and old lead water tanks. Lead levels there were enough to hospitalize the unlucky occupants, who were found to need treatment for chronic lead poisoning. Simultaneous studies in the USA revealed that children with high lead levels were three times more likely to have a low IQ rating (below 80) than were other children.

A startling report by the Greater Glasgow Health Board in 1980 announced that more than 10 per cent of all newborn babies in Glasgow had more lead in their blood than would be considered safe even for fully grown men and women. In 1982 an Edinburgh Council document listed all the 500 water samples taken over the past decade; 33.8 per cent were found to have lead contamination above a safety limit of 100 micrograms per litre (μg/l). In 1981 a survey of women from Ayr found very high levels of lead in the blood of young mothers from the town and connected these lead levels with the rate of mental retardation. Seventy per cent of the town's houses were found to have drinking water that contained more that 100 μg/l.

The longer water stands in a lead pipe, the more lead it will dissolve. If you run a tap for a few minutes and flush the system out, you usually get a lower lead reading. For many years the international scientific and public-health community regarded the figure of 100 μg/l as the safe maximum. The EEC decided in 1980 that it would stick to this figure as the upper limit for lead in drinking water, but it gave a figure of 50 μg/l as the maximum acceptable lead level in a 'flushed' sample of water that had been allowed to run before testing.

However, as we shall see, scientists today are pushing for much lower limits than this, based on up-to-date research into the effects of lead in drinking water. At the very least they want a top figure of 50 μg/l, regardless of the type of sample, as is currently the case in the USA. Many scientists are now pushing for a new international standard of 25 μg/l or even lower. The prestigious American Academy of Science has recommended that 25 μg/l should be adopted as the international standard, but, according to Professor Bryce-Smith, 'Even that would be grossly excessive if used to make up a feed for a baby.' Derek Bryce-Smith has spent twenty years studying the effects of lead. If he says that even a level of 25 μ/l is dangerous for a baby, what was the effect on young Kevin Malone of water containing 160 μg/l of lead? Certainly millions of people every day drink water that contains more lad than 25 μg/l and feed it happily to their babies and children.

Until recently we lived in a modernized Victorian terrace in south Manchester with no obvious lead piping. But our tap water was found to have a reading of 35 μg/l. Frances drank it freely during her pregnancy without a thought and we fed litres of it to our baby twins. If Bryce-Smith and the American Academy of Science are correct, we have already exposed our children to low-dose poisoning that will have some measurable effect on their future intelligence. But we have been lucky compared with the many thousands of British families whose water exceeds the current EEC limit of 50 μg/l and those, like the Malones, who find themselves with even more grossly polluted water.

Some action was taken after the discoveries of the 1970s. In certain areas, including Glasgow, quantities of lime were added to the water supply. Lime is strongly alkaline and so reduces water acidity. The intention was to reduce the amount of lead being dissolved from the antique, crumbling lead water pipes through which the water passed. Glasgow's liming began in 1978 and successfully reduced the amount of lead in the city's water supply. Prior to liming, more than 50 per cent of daytime samples taken at random were found to contain lead levels over the 100 μg/l upper limit. Liming ensured that almost all the city's water scored below 100. In Ayr there was also an improvement after liming, although 10 per cent of samples were still found to have a lead content of over 100 μg/l. The addition of lime to city water supplies was judged a great success. It has doubtless reduced the previously very high lead exposure of thousands of families in Glasgow, Edinburgh and Ayr. But the lead pipes remain, and outside big cities liming is of limited use.

Forty-five kilometres south of Glasgow is the region of Dumfries and Galloway, a community of small towns and villages typical of rural Scotland. Ken Stewart is the director of environmental health for the district council. He was interested in the problem of lead pollution of drinking water in his area, which is noted for its soft, acidic water. However, when he looked for information he quickly discovered that outside a few big cities very little research was being done. So in the early 1980s he decided to do some for himself. In his spare time he walked the streets of Dumfriesshire collecting tap-water samples. What he discovered alarmed him.

Ken Stewart found that of all the houses built before 1964 a third had water-lead levels above the EEC maximum level (for flushed samples) of 50 μg/l. Some families' drinking water had readings of 200 and 300 μg/l. In all, 15 per cent of his samples scored over 100. So-called 'first-draw' samples (water drawn without letting the tap run for a few minutes) were particularly high. Ken Stewart found nobody who had been warned that taps should be run before water was drawn for human consumption.

Ken Stewart has tried to help local families obtain grants to replace their lead plumbing. But the rules are tight. Grants were recently reduced to cover only 75 per cent of the considerable costs involved, and it is not enough simply to identify lead pipes or to find a level of lead in drinking water that would alarm most scientists. To obtain a grant you need a reading of over 100 μg/l – 'far too high', according to Ken Stewart. 'We have had cases where we've taken readings of 70 or 80 and been unable to help these people. This is clearly ridiculous when viewed alongside the latest studies. I don't think it's fair; I don't think it's safe; and I don't think it's right. And I think it is something the government has to address as a matter of some urgency.'

One interesting side-line to Ken Stewart's work is that he found that samples taken from kettles were often higher than tap-water samples, suggesting that some people fill their kettles from the hot-water tap in order to save money. This is particularly dangerous because heat makes water even more 'plumbosolvent', the scientific term for 'likely to dissolve lead'. Nobody with any lead plumbing should ever drink water drawn from the hot-water tap. Ken Stewart also believes that if a kettle is not fully emptied after each boiling, the lead inside it will become more concentrated, exacerbating the problem.

According to Professor Bryce-Smith, Ken Stewart's results in Dumfries are very worrying. 'Two thirds of the samples would be deemed unfit for human consumption by the American Academy of Science, which sets its standard at 25 µg/l, and very few could be considered safe enough to make up a baby's feed.' Pioneer researcher Dr Michael Moore was also concerned at the lead levels discovered by Ken Stewart. 'We've already got some standards saying 50,' he said, 'and United States experts are saying 25 or less, so these levels are certainly worrying. I wouldn't let my children drink that water. In fact, I think public-health measures should be taken to control water like that.'

If an international expert like Dr Michael Moore doesn't want his children drinking this sort of water and thinks that public-health measures should be taken to control its lead level, you might imagine that somebody was advising the people of the area about the problem. Not so. In 1987 *World in Action* contacted the local midwifery service and asked if local mothers were being warned about their drinking water. The midwives were very helpful. The senior community midwife for the area searched her filing cabinet, but all she could produce was a yellowing memorandum from the 1970s advising midwives to tell mothers not to use water from a hot-water tap to make up a baby's feed. From talking to midwives in the area it became clear that they themselves had not been told that local parents were in danger of feeding highly polluted water to their young babies, with serious consequences for the children's mental development. One midwife told us that she was not aware that lead in drinking water was a potential problem in the area: 'It's something that hasn't come up, and we haven't been teaching mothers about that, I'm afraid.' Midwives were not even aware that people should flush their pipes before drawing drinking water, yet this is one of the most simple and effective pieces of advice one can give. We feel sure that in Dumfries this information at least is now given to young families. But how many other areas, unvisited by national television programmes, do likewise?

There was some feverish bureaucratic manoeuvring behind

the scenes when the European Commission was deciding at what level to set the recommended maximum acceptable level for lead in drinking water. Eventually, as we have said, it decided on a figure of 50 μg/l and that this should be judged from a flushed sample. Naturally, this method of sampling means that fewer homes fail to meet the EEC standard, but surely, if the EEC insists on taking its figures from flushed water samples, consumers should be warned to flush their pipes before drinking any water? David Wheeler, of Surrey University's Robens Institute, says that assessing lead levels from a flushed sample 'would be all right provided that people only drank water after the pipes had been flushed. But without a public information campaign to ensure that everybody does that, then surely this is not realistic. A limit should apply to water at the point of consumption – as it comes normally out of the tap.'

Thus we have the pernicious situation in which one arm of government, the Department of the Environment, insists that water-lead levels should be measured from flushed samples, thereby obtaining lower readings, while another arm of government, the Ministry of Health, does not appear to have troubled itself to tell people that flushing would be a good idea. We have certainly seen no evidence of such a public health warning. Professor Bryce-Smith says, 'There has been no general information passed to the public about the importance of flushing pipes. This indicates a remarkable degree of inertia in Whitehall.' Scientists like Bryce-Smith are critical of the British government's role in drafting the EEC guidelines on lead in water. But even after these generous levels were set, the government then asked to delay their implementation in several areas, including the whole of Scotland. The EEC has granted a delay until 1990 for Scotland, Wales, Northern Ireland and parts of England.

Water-authority officials will tell you privately that the problem is not their fault. Their job is to supply water, not domestic plumbing, and they have made efforts to add lime to the water supply. Off the record they question the government's commitment to getting rid of the dangerous lead plumbing itself. For the 5,000 homes in Ken Stewart's area that, he believes, need urgent pipe replacement, only twenty grants have been awarded in recent years. This is due partly to the tightness of the rules and partly to a lack of publicity about the problem. If the most recent research were followed through with new lead limits of, say, 25 μg/l, many more homes would be on the danger list. Ken Stewart knows the scale of the problem in his area because he took the trouble to conduct his own survey, but most local authorities have no clear idea of the extent of lead plumbing in their areas. *World in Action* found high lead readings in random tests in Manchester and Devon, but there are no accurate and up-to-date figures for the country as a whole.

Liming is a short-term solution that works well only in urban areas, and even there the effects are variable. The farther away your house is from the point where the lime is added, the less benefit it is to you. This is because lime does not remain in solution indefinitely, so by the time the water reaches the end of the supply area its effects are considerably reduced. Occasional attempts to 'overdose' the water to compensate have left consumers near the treatment plant complaining of an unpleasant taste in their water.

In spite of liming, high lead readings have persisted. In Glasgow, where liming was thought to have solved the problem, *World in Action* found tap water with lead levels at four, five, even six times the EEC 50 μg/l limit for flushed water samples. The water supplier promised to investigate. Children are most at risk from exposure to lead, so there was a minor political row when, in 1982, the Lothian public analyst reported that nearly half the water samples taken from school drinking fountains in Edinburgh had a lead content of over 100 μg/l. Even after repeated flushing two of the schools' water rated over 500, a remarkably high figure – and this in a city that limes its water. A crash programme to replace pipework in the city's schools soon followed. Edinburgh is a city that is conscious of the lead problem, hence the testing. There must be many other old schools in England, Scotland, Wales and Northern Ireland that are full of lead pipes and whose water has never been tested. Such schools will have seriously lead-poisoned water in their drinking fountains and school kitchens.

All liming programmes are based on the notion of 'safe limits', the assumption that there is a level of lead in drinking water that is scientifically acceptable. Therefore the water authorities simply add lime until they reach that 'safe' level and believe that the problem has been solved. But scientists are discovering that this concept is seriously flawed. Even the small quantities of lead previously assumed to be harmless are now known to be dangerous.

A study in 1987 shocked those scientists who believed that there was such a thing as a safe level of lead exposure. Researchers at Edinburgh University tested the mental abilities of 500 schoolchildren. These children were not exposed to particularly high levels of lead; in fact, their blood-lead levels were less than half those currently regarded as acceptable in Britain. Yet the research demonstrated that even at this low level lead was having an adverse effect on their learning ability as assessed by tests in numerical, verbal, spatial and short-term memory skills. Taking a British ability level of 100, the researchers found that children with higher blood-lead levels in the group were 6 per cent down, even allowing for variables such as social advantage. Lead was knocking up to 6 per cent off their intelligence. Lead in tap water, the research team believed, was the most important source of this blood lead, and they concluded that there should now be no level of lead exposure that could be considered safe.

One of the researchers, Mary Fulton, has said, 'When we started this research we were not ideologically committed to lead being very harmful or not harmful. We were very open-minded about it ... I would certainly have expected the effect to be small, and probably not even observable.' But observable it was. Of course, many factors influence a person's intelligence, but here is evidence that seemingly harmless tap water with a low lead content is undermining children's normal mental development. Responding to the survey, Dr Gerald Forbes, a government medical officer, said, 'Questions will be asked as to whether the present limit of lead in blood and in water is adequate.'

These new statistics suggest that many urban children have some mental handicap due to lead. The blood-lead levels of the Edinburgh children were the same as those identified in London and other major cities. Both drinking water and fumes from petrol play a part, but, whatever the source, it is now clear that lead at any level is a serious threat to children. As Mary Fulton summed up in cold, scientific language: 'There is a dose-response relation with no evidence of a threshold or safe level ... Although our results require some caution in their interpretation, as do all data from observational studies, they are in accord with other findings and suggest that steps already being taken to reduce exposure to lead should be continued and, indeed, reinforced.'

These findings are supported by equally alarming work done recently in the USA. At Harvard Medical School researchers found that babies whose blood lead was well within current British standards were having their speech, memory and learning potential damaged. If we extrapolate from the work at Harvard, the conclusion is that hundreds of thousands of babies are being born in this country every year with enough lead in their bodies to retard their natural mental development.

Blood lead is measured in micrograms per decilitre. In Britain the Department of Health says that the safe, or 'action', level for lead in blood is 25 micrograms per decilitre. But the Harvard team, led by Dr David Bellinger, has discovered that mental development is impaired at 10 micrograms per decilitre or even less. They took blood samples from 249 Boston babies at birth and tracked the children for two years. Children with blood-lead levels over 10 micrograms scored 5 per cent less well in monthly mental tests than those with under 3 micrograms. The best scientific evidence from Britain is that many, perhaps most, children are born with lead levels of at least 10 micrograms per decilitre in their blood. A study by Dr Richard Lownsdown and Dr William Yule found that 142 of 166 children tested in Greenwich had blood-lead levels of over 10 micrograms per decilitre. Dr Michael Moore, whose discoveries in the 1970s first proved the dangers of lead in tap water, has been amazed by the new findings: 'In the past I would have been doubtful, but these two widely separated studies suggest that whole populations are several intelligence points down. I used to think we needed to reduce the levels of lead in the water, but now I feel that there probably can be no safe level.'

There was, in fact, a Royal Commission into the problems of lead pollution in 1983. Its sensible recommendations about lead in drinking water make depressing reading because there is little evidence that anything has been done about them. Among other suggestions left lying on the shelf, the Commissioners called for the government to 'set an early and firm target date for completion of surveys to identify plumbo-solvency in water supplied for human consumption and of remedial treatment or pipe replacement.' There was also the recommendation that 'The criteria for the award of home improvement or repair grants for the replacement of lead plumbing should be reviewed, with the aim of making such grants more widely available.' Furthermore, the Commission recognized that 'Publicity campaigns should be conducted in areas where pipe replacement is considered necessary' and that 'Financial constraints should not be allowed to hamper the pipe replacement programme.' If anything, the government appears to have done the reverse. Professor Bryce-Smith talks of 'an outstanding example of blindness in government . . . Lip-service is paid to protecting the environment especially when it's thought that votes might be involved, but the government is most reluctant to spend money on making a truly better and less toxic environment for its citizens.'

The problem is one of human nature. As Ken Stewart found in Dumfries, people are not keen to find large sums of money to replace their own plumbing unless they can see a very good reason. It is hard for individual environmental health officers to persuade people that this is a serious matter when there is no national urgency about the problem. Without a firm lead from the government, why should individuals incur the trouble and the expense of replacing their plumbing or going through the bureaucratic fuss of applying for a grant, especially if they are in short-term accommodation anyway?

Lead does its damage slowly and imperceptibly. The water probably looks fine and tastes fine. Without publicity campaigns it is hard for people to believe that it may be harming them. After *World in Action* featured Stella and Kevin Malone and their young family, they were quickly rehoused. But who is living there now? Probably one of the thousands of families who every day unwittingly poison their own children.

Some countries are pushing for lower and lower lead levels to be set. It seems unlikely that Britain has the will to meet even the current, discredited, levels. One section of the population is undoubtedly becoming more lead-conscious – the motorist is urged, in hard-hitting campaigns, to switch to unleaded petrol. But we should also be tackling the source of lead that is closest to home: our drinking water. What is urgently needed is a co-ordinated campaign to alert people to the dangers. If they only knew the risks, many families would use their own money to replace lead pipes. For those who need help, the government must make more generous grants available, on less rigid conditions, to help people rip out their poisonous pipes once and for all.

Intelligence is not just a matter of scoring on an IQ test. People's intelligence affects their personality, their career, their whole life. It is also a national asset. Dr Michael Moore sums up gloomily: 'We are a lead-damaged nation, there is no doubt; we have generations of people who are not achieving, and will not achieve, their full potential because of lead. As a country our quality of life is reduced and our national performance is undermined in a competitive world.'

3

A CASE OF DELAYED REACTION

Aluminium in drinking water

You might compare it to the link between smoking and lung cancer.
We're at about the same stage as research on smoking and lung
cancer was twenty years ago.
Dr Philip Day, Department of Chemistry, Manchester University, 1988

Most of the chemicals in our drinking water have got there
more by accident than design. Nobody is deliberately pouring
lead or pesticides or industrial waste straight into the mains.
But aluminium is different. The water authorities add the chemical themselves, tipping it in by the tonne. Every year they add
100,000 tonnes of aluminium sulphate to drinking-water supplies
in order to help purify the water. This process, called flocculation, causes impurities to coagulate and sink to the bottom of
giant tanks. Aluminium flocculation leaves water looking clean
and sparkling when it pours out of the tap. Unfortunately there
is now growing evidence that a high aluminium content in
drinking water appears to contribute to bone disease, making
bones weaken and fracture spontaneously. In the north of
England, where there are high levels of aluminium in the water,
the incidence of bone disease is also high. There is also evidence
that aluminium, like lead, is causing serious damage to our
brains and that it is partly responsible for one of the most
common and most distressing illnesses of our times, Alzheimer's
Disease.

Lead damages the brains of the young; aluminium is thought
to damage the brains of the old. Alzheimer's Disease affects
well over half a million people in this country. In the words of
Dr Jonathan Miller, the President of the Alzheimer's Disease
Society, it is 'a particularly cruel, progressive brain disease in
which the ability to remember, to learn, to think, to reason,

gradually deteriorates. By the end, the brain is to all intents and purposes a dead, useless organ. This is a disease that can strike anybody. It attacks all races, all classes. There is not the slightest glimmer of light at the end of the tunnel.'

In early 1989 a Medical Research Council study, conducted by Dr Christopher Martin of Southampton University, offered strong evidence of a link between high levels of aluminium in drinking water and a high incidence of Alzheimer's Disease. Water samples were taken from around England and Wales. The higher the level of aluminium, the greater the risk of getting the disease. These findings do not prove that aluminium causes Alzheimer's, but the statistics are certainly worrying, particularly when you consider that none of the samples in the study was outside current EEC limits. It is even more worrying when you realize that, like so many other chemicals, aluminium is often present in British drinking water at levels way above EEC limits.

More evidence of a link between aluminium and diseases of the brain comes from an internal report by Surrey University's Chemistry Department. The study, carried out in 1987, found high levels of aluminium in drinking water. Comparing these levels with the incidence of Alzheimer's Disease around the country, they concluded: 'The high levels of dementia do in some cases reflect the areas of high-aluminium water content.'

It has been difficult to pinpoint the cause of Alzheimer's Disease. It seems to be connected with getting old, yet not all old people have it. Sometimes it seems to run in families, but only in the minority of cases. It seems to have something to do with aluminium in drinking water, yet not everyone who drinks high-aluminium tap water gets the disease. The Alzheimer's Disease Society feels that the effects of aluminium should be further investigated. Noreen Miller, the Society's director, told us, 'A lot of members and carers are very concerned about aluminium. When we first heard about the Southampton study we tabled questions to the House of Commons asking for as much investigation as possible.' The Water Authorities Association has reacted rather more calmly. Although 'growing concern' was expressed, the *Water Bulletin* of 17 June

1988 assured us: 'Drinking water containing aluminium is safe to drink and links with Alzheimer's Disease are not proven.' Well, there may not be firm proof yet, but there are other reasons why it is thought that aluminium may be a cause of Alzheimer's Disease and why the water authorities should take the problem a great deal more seriously.

First, there's what is found in the brain of someone who has died from the disease. Basically, there are two characteristic lesions: the senile plaque, a minute area of brain damage; and the neurofibrillary tangle, a deposit of protein fibrils in damaged nerve cells. In both of these there are deposits of aluminium. This doesn't mean that aluminium has necessarily caused the damage, but it certainly looks suspicious. Secondly, injections of aluminium into animals have been shown to cause severe memory loss. When the unfortunate animals are dissected, they are found to have Alzheimer's-type 'tangles' in their brains. Thirdly, it has been known for a long time that aluminium can produce 'dialysis dementia', with symptoms similar to those of Alzheimer's Disease, in kidney-dialysis patients. Doctors in the 1970s noticed that kidney patients using high-aluminium water for dialysis tended to become demented. Some died of aluminium poisoning. Special filters were introduced to remove the aluminium and other impurities from the water, and the rate of dialysis dementia dropped.

In the USA aluminium is regarded as a likely cause of Alzheimer's Disease. American researchers have found that people living on aluminium-rich islands in the Pacific often develop similar illnesses. In Scandinavia too researchers have published evidence of high rates of Alzheimer's Disease in those areas where the water contains raised levels of aluminium. Even as all this evidence has been building up, it has taken an inordinately long time for anyone to get worried. For years the warning signs have been there. The toxicity of aluminium was first noted in the late 1960s, and the dangers for kidney patients have been documented for ten years. Couldn't someone have carried out a few studies before? Isn't it now time for the water authorities to investigate other ways of flocculating their water supplies?

One problem is that aluminium is very common. There is so much of it about that until recently it was not considered an interesting enough subject for study. It is also difficult to measure accurately in blood. Furthermore, drinking water is not the only source of aluminium in the diet. In fact, it is not even the main one. The average person in this country consumes 5–10 milligrams of aluminium every day. It is present in baking powder, instant coffee, dried milk, tea, aspirin and antacids. In processed foods its presence is indicated by the E numbers E173, E541, E554 and E556. It can also be dissolved from aluminium cooking pans and tins, particularly if they are used to cook acid foods such as stewed fruit or anything containing vinegar. But however much aluminium we get from our diet, it is the aluminium in drinking water that seems to cause the problems. According to Neil Ward of the Robens Institute, it seems that most of the sources of aluminium are not bio-available and cannot easily be absorbed into the human body. It is possible that aluminium is more potent in water because, like lead, it is already in suspension and can quickly pass into the bloodstream through the gut wall. Tea contains plenty of aluminium, but it also contains fluoride, which, some scientists believe, prevents aluminium from being absorbed.

Few people are aware of the links between aluminium in drinking water and Alzheimer's Disease, and this, above all, accounts for the lack of urgency in connection with the topic. It is a fact of political life that publicity is a critical element in any health campaign. Media coverage whips up public concern and pressurizes politicians and officials into being seen to be 'doing something' about problem X. Under these political conditions money and public-health initiatives can be conjured out of thin air, as happened in 1988–9 with the problem of salmonella in the poultry industry and with listeria contamination of cook-chill foods. The problem with Alzheimer's Disease is, to put it crudely, that sick old people do not make good newspaper copy or good television. A mother loses a baby through listeria, and the popular press, quite rightly, is up in arms. Thousands of people suffer from Alzheimer's Disease, a disease clearly linked with a chemical in drinking water, and few newspapers seem to notice.

It seems clear that current evidence justifies urgent action to phase out the widespread use of the chemical in water treatment. At the moment, however, water authorities are resisting such pressure and are quick to draw attention to the other sources of aluminium in our diet. (Shortly after the Southampton study came to public attention, a spokesman for Southern Water said on the radio that maybe those in the study who were suffering from dementia had drunk a lot of tea. Whether the spokesman didn't understand the nature of the study is uncertain. Obviously in such a scientific study all variables are eliminated, and no evidence has been found that tea-drinking causes Alzheimer's Disease. But it is the kind of argument that sounds superficially plausible.) Some consumers are considering suing their water authorities over aluminium in their drinking water. A former mayor of Bideford in Devon, Peter Christie, is, at the time of writing, attempting to take South West Water to court for public nuisance, negligence and breach of contract. Mr Christie was alerted to the problem of aluminium by Christopher Martin's recent Southampton University report and discovered that Cornwall has one of the highest concentrations of aluminium in drinking water.

There are other theories concerning the causes of Alzheimer's Disease: it may be partly genetically determined, and it is clearly something to do with getting old. Professor J. Edwardson, an expert on the illness, has written: 'The most reasonable hypothesis would be that some individuals have a genetic predisposition which makes them more vulnerable to environmental factors such as aluminium.' It is also possible that, as we get older, our ability to cope with aluminium decreases.

Despite all the evidence, the official line is still that it is not worth doing anything until a link is proven. Yet proof positive is not easy to come by. Dr Ruth Itzhaki of the University of Manchester Institute of Science and Technology says, 'It's very hard to prove that aluminium causes Alzheimer's Disease. You can't do experiments on humans, for ethical reasons.' Nobody would expect volunteers to consume high levels of aluminium just to see if their brains become damaged. So evidence such as the Southampton study is invaluable in the search for a possible cause. Dr Philip Day of Manchester University told us, 'You might compare it to the link between smoking and lung cancer. We're at about the same stage as research on smoking and lung cancer was twenty years ago.'

If proof of a link were to appear, aluminium would have to be banned from use in water treatment. At the moment the very least we should do is to stick to the current EEC limits for aluminium in drinking water. But we do not. The EEC has set a maximum value for aluminium in water of 200 micrograms per litre (μg/l), with a guideline value of 50 μg/l. But in many parts of the country these values are greatly exceeded. When *World in Action* carried out its tests on lead levels in Scottish drinking water, it was surprised to find that the levels of aluminium were also very high: nearly two thirds of the samples were above the EEC maximum admissible concentration, and a fifth were more than double the limit. This finding matches that of Surrey University's internal report, which said that not just some but the *majority* of British water authorities provide domestic tap water that at times exceeds EEC limits for aluminium, especially in Scotland and the north of England. According to Dr Philip Day, 'We have detected tap-water levels of aluminium of up to 2,000 μg/l in Stockport and 1,000 μg/l in Newcastle. The EEC limit is just 200.' The recent Southampton research involved people whose water was well below the EEC limit, yet exposure to these legal levels of aluminium is thought by the researchers to increase the risk of Alzheimer's Disease. In the light of this evidence, the limits may have to be revised.

The government's immediate reaction to the EEC limits was to apply for exemptions. Millions of people in Scotland, Wales and the north and west of England receive water that is exempted from the EEC limits; the government recognizes that the standards just can't be met. Exemptions, however, are supposed to be allowed only on grounds of 'exceptional geographical or meteorological conditions'; one could hardly claim that this is the case with aluminium, which is deliberately added to the water. Only in a few places does aluminium occur naturally: if the soil is particularly acidic – for example, in parts of Yorkshire – or if the area is subject to acid rain that causes aluminium in the soil to be dissolved into the water.

In some parts of the country it would be relatively easy to reduce aluminium levels. There are other substances that could be used to flocculate and purify the water. But elsewhere, where the high aluminium levels are due to acid soil or acid rain, expensive treatment systems would have to be installed. Against the likely cost of this should be set the current costs of caring for dementia patients: £2 billion a year for the NHS, a cost that is bound to increase as our population ages and a larger proportion of us suffer from the diseases of old age. There is also the financial and emotional cost to relatives and friends of sufferers to consider.

For those already suffering from Alzheimer's Disease, it's too late to do anything. The damage has already been done. For the rest of us, we can only hope that complacency will give way to action.

4
THE DUSTBIN OF EUROPE
Hazardous-waste disposal in Britain

The flow of waste into this country is not a bad thing.
Lord Caithness, Environment Minister, 1988

I don't understand why the British government is allowing it in.
George Baker, Canadian MP, on British imports of Canadian waste,
1988

The ease with which anyone with a lorry can set himself up as a
disposal contractor is alarming.
House of Lords Committee, 1981

We produce thousands of tonnes of waste every year in this
country. Some of it is the household rubbish we put out in
black bags for the bin men to collect. Some is builder's rubble.
Some is scrap metal. And then there's the nasty stuff – the
chemicals that come in drums with a skull and crossbones on
the side, the tankers marked 'danger', waste that is toxic and
unstable and needs to be disposed of very carefully.

Very little of this is recycled – probably as little as 15 per
cent.[1] Most of it goes to landfill. In other words, we take the
waste and fill up our land with it. It's cheap and convenient,
and there are plenty of holes in the ground that need filling up.
Perhaps 'disposal' is the wrong word for most of what goes on.
The hazardous chemicals do not disappear; instead they are put
where nobody can see them. The hope is that they will go away.
Unfortunately they do not, and some of them have a disagree-
able habit of making their way into the public water supply.

Hazardous-waste management in this country is a national
disgrace – or, rather, it would be if more people were aware of
the scandalous state of affairs. When you consider that drinking
water is a finite resource and that less than 0.01 per cent of the
global water reserve is suitable for human consumption, our
reliance on 'out of sight, out of mind' hazardous-waste manage-

ment techniques, like landfill, seems absurd. Already 10 per cent of Britain's underground aquifers are no longer used for drinking water because of heavy contamination with dangerous chemicals thought to have leaked, in part, from waste dumps.

The British hazardous-waste disposal business is run by hundreds of private companies, logged locally but not nationally. There are over 5,600 private site licences currently in operation. These licences are issued by waste-disposal authorities, usually part of the local authority. Private firms need to make a profit. The temptation to cut corners or not to ask too many questions about waste is ever-present, particularly as the regulation and inspection of these sites is not what it should be. Far from it. The national Hazardous Waste Inspectorate (HWI) said in June 1988 that while considerable improvements had been made at many sites, 'The contrast between the best and worst remains as bad as ever.' The inspectors' last report into Britain's whole system of hazardous-waste disposal was subtitled 'Ramshackle and Antediluvian', hardly a sign that they have much confidence in the present profit-led system.

The usual method of disposing of hazardous waste by landfill is to mix it with household rubbish. This dilutes it somewhat, and, as the other rubbish decomposes, some hazardous waste can be beneficially transformed. In theory there should be no problem. Hallmarks of the bad waste contractors, however, include poorly chosen sites, no lining of the ground before dumping takes place, shoddy finishing and capping of the site and, most important, poor aftercare, which means minimal, if any, monitoring for leakage and gas escapes. In fact, companies can make their money and then just walk away from their sites, hand in their licences and move on elsewhere. This leaves the local authority and the local community to live with the consequences of their sloppy and dangerous waste management. The worst firms, so-called cowboy operators, threaten to lower everybody's standards and seem able to flout the rules with impunity.

Britain is currently acquiring quite a reputation abroad for being a good place to dispose of hazardous waste. In the summer of 1988 a tremendous fuss was made about a ship called the *Karin B*. It was loaded with 2,000 tonnes of highly toxic waste, reportedly in leaky containers and certainly not properly documented. An attempt was made to land the waste in this country. Government ministers went on television and made speeches vowing that we would not accept this dangerous cargo. 'Britain will not be a dustbin for other people's dangerous rubbish', the British people were assured. But Britain already is an international dustbin. As a nation we specialize in waste disposal. We take waste from the Netherlands, Belgium, Ireland, America, Australia, Singapore and other nations. No other Western country imports rubbish on such a scale. In fact, apart from some Eastern Bloc and Third World countries, Britain is the world's only significant importer of waste. It's a growing industry: in 1981 we imported 4,000 tonnes of toxic waste (or 'special' waste, as it is known in the trade). In 1987, 53,000 tonnes were officially imported (and more came in unannounced).

Whether the waste is foreign or domestic, there is frequently commercial pressure to choose landfill rather than more ecologically friendly methods of disposal. The HWI reported on one operator who had a contract to dispose of some acid and alkaline waste. He proposed to treat it before dumping, but a competitor came along and offered to landfill the waste at a cheaper price. The original contractor had either to lose this valuable contract or adopt the cheaper landfill option himself. He chose to landfill, and 2,500 tonnes per annum of acid at pH1 and alkali at pH8 were poured directly into the ground rather than being treated.

A popular method of avoiding the costly treatment of waste is to dilute it until its concentration is just inside the legal limit for landfill. The HWI is aware of two cases in which dangerous, low-flash-point solvent wastes were deliberately diluted so they would be within licence conditions. There is also the problem of the improper labelling of drums of toxic waste: HWI reports speak of 'sealed drums of undetermined contents' being dumped in the ground. No one knows how many drums are involved, but the HWI says, 'We know that tens of thousands annually represents the order of magnitude.'

This is not necessarily the site operator's fault. The company is, to an extent, at the mercy of its customers. If a customer lies about a consignment, there is little the contractor can do. However, there is sometimes the suspicion that some site operators avoid asking their customers too many awkward questions, thereby attracting just the kind of customer who wants to dispose of difficult loads of chemicals with the minimum of fuss and no questions asked. For example, an order form may specify nitric acid at 1 per cent, but if the barrels arrive containing 30 per cent nitric acid, how many contractors will return the consignment, and risk losing future business, when there is a big hole to be filled up and little chance that anybody will ever find out exactly what has been poured into it? Moreover, the site operator is occasionally not even sure where the waste has come from in the first place. Waste is not always dealt with by the contractor who first takes it away. Sometimes it is sent to transfer stations subcontracted to a different company altogether.

For example, some scientific research waste, spontaneously flammable in air or water, was sold to a company for disposal by incineration. The price was £1,350 plus VAT. However, the company subcontracted the waste to a transfer-station operator at a price of £187. The operator then further subcontracted it to a landfill operator for £75. At three stages removed from the original sale, who was to know that landfill was dangerous? Luckily the local waste-disposal authority was aware of the situation and intercepted the waste before dumping could take place. This story is a good example of the danger inherent in the poorly regulated waste-disposal business. There are certainly conscientious operators and dealers, but too many people seem to trade in toxic waste as unscrupulous garage owners trade in second-hand cars. There must be many occasions when similar shady deals result in the pouring of dangerous waste into landfill sites.

The operation of a site does not end when the last load is dumped. There is then the considerable problem of how to deal with the liquid that escapes from such a site, known as the 'leachate'. There is also the need to deal with gas produced by the waste. The National Association of Waste Disposal

Contractors (NAWDC) calculates that approximately 3–5 per cent of a site's revenue should be set aside for aftercare. But some companies do not want to spend that kind of money years, even decades, after they have been paid. So they simply hand in their licence and walk away from the site, as the current system allows them to do. It is the waste-disposal authority and, ultimately, the public who have to pick up the bill.

The NAWDC aims to improve the standards and the image of the waste-disposal business. It has about sixty full members, and, according to David Boyd, the organization represents 'the top end of the business, mostly large firms but also some smaller ones'. Boyd is disparaging about some operators: 'There are some people in the industry you wouldn't go near with a bargepole.' The NAWDC turns down applicants if they are felt to be not up to scratch, but smaller outfits can sometimes undercut NAWDC members, with the result that they too are tempted to economize. We rang a few waste-disposal authorities to ask whether prosecutions were generally of NAWDC members or of the so-called cowboy outfits. The reply was always 'A bit of both.' One company mentioned was Leigh Environmental, whose Group Services managing director, Edward Wilkinson, was recently appointed chairman of the NAWDC disciplinary committee. The Leigh Group is certainly well established, yet it has a history of prosecutions for infringements of environmental and safety laws. In January 1989 Leigh Land Reclamation was convicted for twelve infringements of the Control of Pollution Act. There is a vigorous local campaign to close one of the company's landfill sites in Walsall, used for industrial waste.

Anxiety increases in the light of some of the chemicals that are disposed of. Modern industrial chemistry has developed many thousands of new products over the last few decades. Scientists are only now beginning to realize just how dangerous some of these man-made chemicals can be. Take polychlorinated biphenyls (PCBs) as an example. PCBs were very useful: they were once employed extensively in the electrical industry as insulating material and also in adhesives, flame-proof fabrics, printing inks, paints and pesticides. They were not thought to be particularly dangerous at first, and well over 1 million tonnes were produced before it was realized that PCBs are among the most poisonous chemicals ever made. Even a minuscule exposure damages any organic life. Production was banned in 1977, but until 1985 many countries were still producing the chemicals. The problem of safe disposal remains. PCBs do not occur naturally and cannot be disposed of naturally. Instead of breaking down, they accumulate in living cells and may cause cells to produce self-damaging toxins or cancer-causing proteins.

Some PCBs have already entered the environment through earlier dumping of industrial and commercial waste. Inevitably some are leaking out and entering food chains. The chemicals were implicated in the mysterious and deadly seal disease that became evident in 1988; PCBs do not cause the disease, but it is thought that they make seals more vulnerable and affect their ability to recover. Hundreds of dead seals have made a powerful impression on people who had remained unshaken by earlier reports of dead and diseased fish in our oceans. The suggestion that pollution is killing seals, a sophisticated mammal biologically similar to human beings, has alarmed many people and has heightened concern about the entry of dangerous chemicals into our water environment.

It is believed that over 250,000 tonnes of PCBs remain in use;[2] these will eventually have to be disposed of. The only safe way to do this is to incinerate the chemicals at over 1,000°C, a very expensive form of waste management. In this country it is still legal to dump PCB-contaminated materials, provided the concentration is less than 500 parts per million. Some waste inspectors believe that there are firms that dilute their PCBs to just below this limit to avoid expensive incineration costs. If they are put into a landfill, there is the obvious danger of leakage into the soil and water system. In 1986 researchers from the University of East Anglia conducted a major survey into PCB contamination of soil samples. Samples were taken from ordinary soil, not just from tips and areas likely to be contaminated. The chemicals were found to be present in every one of the ninety-five samples analysed, with the highest concentrations in or near cities. The figures were small, but PCBs accumulate over time and do not decay. The research was conclusive proof that much of the country is already thoroughly contaminated with small quantities of these deadly chemicals.

Frequently it is not clear whether a consignment of waste contains PCBs or other dangerous toxic chemicals, especially if the waste has come from abroad. The figure for Britain's runaway growth in imports of hazardous waste (some 53,000 tonnes in 1987) represents just the material that comes under the government's definition of 'special' waste. Britain actually imports a great deal more 'non-special' waste, which is not subject to the same regulations. Exactly how much is shipped to Britain, or what exactly is in each consignment, remains vague. The HWI estimated that 183,000 tonnes of such waste entered this country for disposal in 1986–7.

Waste disposal seems a curious business for Britain to specialize in. Many of the countries that send their waste here are much larger than Britain, and you might think that they had the necessary space in which to get rid of their own rubbish. (Britain is one of the most densely populated countries on the planet.) Yet it appears that the cost of disposing of toxic waste in this country is cheap compared with the cost elsewhere in Western Europe. The HWI describes one local authority on the south coast that handles 1,000 lorry-loads of imported special waste every year. Dump trucks come over on the morning ferry and return home, empty, the same evening. In 1988 a Canadian MP said that Britain was foolish to accept his country's toxic waste. Mr George Baker warned that large quantities of highly toxic chemicals, including PCBs, regularly made their way across the Atlantic. 'I don't understand why the British government is allowing it in,' he said.

Britain specializes in taking in other people's waste partly, it is said, because its disposal technology leads the world. It may comfort the patriotic reader to learn that Britain's waste dumps are the envy of Europe, but we suspect not. Perhaps a more important reason for rocketing waste imports is that Britain is regarded as a soft touch. Compared with countries such as France and West Germany, we certainly are; neither of these two nations allows the import of poisonous waste for disposal on a commercial basis. The British government's attitude is simple: if the system is adequate, it does not matter where the waste is coming from. Britain is turning muck into brass. In the words of Lord Caithness, the Environment Minister, 'The flow of waste into this country is not a bad thing.'

Leigh Interests even considered dealing with the waste on board the infamous *Karin B.* Leigh's Group Services director said at the time, 'Someone has got to sort this material out, and we can.' This may be fair enough. If British firms have the technology to deal responsibly with an international waste crisis that no one else can manage, perhaps they should be allowed to do so – but only, surely, as an occasional act of good will. The reality of most waste importing, however, has little to do with high technology. Much of the hazardous waste currently flooding into Britain is hardly intended for treatment at all. The HWI says that many waste imports receive only the most rudimentary treatment before being dumped into holes in the ground.

At the time of the *Karin B.* crisis one government Environment minister had the nerve to proclaim, 'The UK has rigorous laws governing importation of dangerous waste', a statement that must have amazed the government's own hazardous-waste inspectors, who have been arguing for years that Britain's laws are fundamentally unsound. Even Sir Hugh Rossi, Conservative chairman of the Commons Environment Committee, has described waste-management regulation as 'pretty shambolic'. While the *Karin B.* was moored off the coast of Britain, an editorial in the *Guardian* thundered: 'Britain's record in disposing of dangerous wastes is a disgrace. We are known as the dirty old man of Europe because the world knows it can dump just about anything on us and we'll get rid of it, as often as not without knowing precisely what it is, let alone what it might be doing to our environment. We do it cheaper than anyone else because, crudely, we cut a lot of corners and our laws are inadequate.' The Institute of Waste Management has also said that it is 'concerned about the increasing quantities of contaminated material being brought into this country for disposal directly to landfill, sometimes following rejection of the material for landfilling in the country of origin'. The Institute's president, Dennis Taylor, has recently called for urgent government action to stop Britain from becoming the 'dustbin of Europe'.

David Boyd, of the National Association of Waste Disposal Contractors, defends waste imports. He says that some countries have few suitable landfill sites because of their geology. Others have what he calls over-restrictive legislation. 'If [disposal is] done with the proper controls, there is no need to fear,' says Boyd.

Yet some waste comes in more or less secretly. When the ferry *Herald of Free Enterprise* capsized in 1987 salvage workers were amazed to find drums of toxic waste on board. Most dangerous were sixty drums of cyanide solution, one of which exploded, injuring four rescue workers. This cargo was being shipped to Britain for disposal. The driver said that he didn't know what was in the drums; the ferry company said that it had not been told that the lorry contained toxic waste; and the importer said he thought that the cargo was going on a freight ferry. How many other ships are coming in full of toxic waste about which nothing is known? Certainly the HWI believes that documentation accompanying shipments is often 'cursory and inadequate'. A recent incident illustrates the shadowy side of the international waste business and what regulators and inspectors are up against. In November 1988 a British company was approached by the *Sunday Times*. Two reporters claimed to represent a chemical firm wanting to export dangerous waste to Africa. They secretly recorded the company's managing director giving his prospective clients the following advice: 'We don't want to know what is really on board. You can give us a false invoice on false headed paper. Nobody will ask any questions. We have about fifty local officials whom we pay each month to keep their mouths shut. Even if it is radioactive, it doesn't matter ... If anything happens to the Africans because of the waste, that's too bad. It's not our problem.'

Companies that break the law can, of course, be prosecuted. In 1988 a waste transfer-station operator was fined £500 plus

£1,300 costs after drums from the station were examined. They were found to contain unsolidified face cream concealing 118 laboratory bottles of hazardous waste from the electronics and metal-finishing industries. But it is not at all easy to bring a prosecution. If operators object, they can continue to work until their cases are heard, which may not be for many months. Keith Bratley, chief waste-disposal officer in West Yorkshire, asked in the *Institute of Waste Management Bulletin* in November 1984: 'Would it not be in the public interest for the site operator to prove that his proposals or operations are safe?' He also criticized the vagueness of the wording of the Control of Pollution Act 1974, in which words and phrases like 'adequate', 'reasonable satisfaction' and 'suitable facilities' are used. Because of the difficulty of proving cases and enforcing the law, the legislation has in some quarters been labelled a cowboys' charter.

Waste-disposal authorities are supposed to be supervised by the HWI, now incorporated into HM Inspectorate of Pollution. In May 1988 the Chief Inspector, David Mills, resigned in protest at the poor progress that had been made in raising waste-management standards. He had written three consecutive annual reports pressing for changes in the law to drive out cowboy waste dumpers. At a press conference he said, 'They were all equally critical, but there was no significant improvement, and no significant measures were taken.' Some of David Mills's suggestions have been raised in report after report, stretching back to the early 1970s. One reason why the government will not act, he feels, is that environmental protection is not a high-profile issue: 'The environment has just not seemed sexy, and it hasn't been found time.' Shortly before his resignation David Mills said that he needed many more inspectors. In 1987 the Inspectorate had only five inspectors to oversee 5,000 sites. They managed to visit only 225 that year. What little information is collected is jealously guarded by Whitehall officials. Sir Hugh Rossi's Commons Environment Committee recently attacked the Department of the Environment for refusing to name local authorities that have 'abysmal' records with respect to waste sites. Sir Hugh told government Environment

Minister and fellow Tory Lord Caithness that it was 'disgraceful' that his Department had failed to ensure that waste-disposal authorities did their job properly.

Back in 1981 Lord Gregson's House of Lords Committee had called for much tighter regulations in the waste-disposal business, saying, 'The ease with which anyone with a lorry can set himself up as a disposal contractor is alarming.' The government has not been able to find the parliamentary time to enact Lord Gregson's recommendations. Politics is a matter of priorities, and environmental protection has clearly come low on the list in the 1980s. As the months drag on, and as hazardous waste accumulates in ill-managed dumps, recommendations like Lord Gregson's gather dust on the shelf.

In the USA the system is very different. Companies found guilty of illegal dumping in California, for example, are made to advertise the fact, at considerable expense – 'Illegal dumping is wrong. We should know. We got caught!' We put this suggestion to a number of waste-disposal authorities and contractors. Their reactions ranged from 'Lovely!' and 'That's an interesting one. I'd be happy to try anything!' to 'Well, we don't really need that here' (this comment from a contractor).

The HWI declares: 'If we have avoided major problems with co-disposal landfill in the UK, the Inspectorate considers that in some cases this is due more to luck than judgement.' It compares a dumping site to a living creature: 'Some of the licences which we have seen are not concerned adequately to control its diet, whether qualitatively or quantitively, nor to monitor its subsequent digestion, excretion and overall well-being.' One survey of thirty-five major landfill sites found that less than half of the site licences required any sort of observation wells or boreholes for monitoring the water beneath the sites. The inspectors concluded, 'It is legitimate to question the value of many of the licences in terms of environmental protection.' From many such reports by clearly dissatisfied inspectors and local officials a depressing picture emerges of the bad side of Britain's waste-disposal industry. No one knows what's being put into some of these dumps. No one is monitoring the leachate to see what's coming out. There aren't enough inspectors to go round. And the cowboys are able to get away with murder.

Just as some tips are badly run now, others were badly run in the past. Even if new and stricter regulations were brought in tomorrow and the number of inspectors increased dramatically, there will still be pollution from these older sites in the future. Until 1972 there were no special arrangements for the dumping of hazardous waste. In the early 1970s there were stories of toxic waste being poured into cellars. Leachate from waste like this is now finding its way into our drinking-water supplies. Waste-disposal officer Keith Bratley has written: 'There are instances of severe environmental pollution from this uncontrolled state of affairs prior to 1972.' Bob Harris of Severn Trent Water Authority admits that old tips are 'a problem because no one is responsible for them'.

It is impossible to estimate the number of such sites. A tip closed down thirty years ago could still be producing poisonous leachate. Frequently no record was kept of the nature of the waste being dumped. Geoff Williams of the British Geological Survey (BGS) believes that 'You can't put millions of tonnes of waste into the ground without some contamination of water.' Recently in Luton and Dunstable a high concentration of trichloroethylene was found in the drinking water. Nobody has been able to determine where it is coming from. In 1988, the BGS said 'Landfills, with the variety of contaminants they produce, threaten numerous [water] sources . . . Currently available information suggests that as sampling and analytical techniques develop, the occurrence of organic contaminants in groundwater will be shown to be more widespread.' Bob Harris told us that a number of urban streams were polluted from old tips in the Severn Trent area. Obviously the water authority does not use these for drinking-water supplies, but leachate can easily migrate through the soil. In Nottinghamshire the borehole supplying the village of Harworth had to be closed down when leachate from an old coke-making plant migrated 1 kilometre towards the village.

John Mather of the BGS explained why pollution of groundwater is so serious: 'It's not like a river, with other water pushing it down and flushing it away. It takes a lot longer for any pollution to be flushed out.' An aquifer in Kent was recently polluted by leachate from an old mine forty-five years after the original contamination; the local water pumping station still cannot be used. Andy Booth of Greenpeace points out, 'Ten per cent of Britain's underground aquifers which used to provide a vital source of drinking water are now unfit for human consumption. They're officially closed because they contain cancer-causing agents.'

More recycling of toxic waste would reduce the risks of poorly regulated dumping. However, we may be recycling less waste in years to come. Waste inspectors believe that Britain's existing recycling capacity is under threat precisely because landfill-site licences permit the large-scale pouring of concentrated and reactive wastes directly into the ground. The Institute of Waste Management says, 'Central government encourages recycling in principle but does not interfere with market forces.' In other words, the politicians are happy to leave things as they are. It is only if government interferes by making recycling competitive that other options will be chosen in preference to landfill. Meanwhile the dump trucks keep arriving; the inspectors get angrier and angrier; chemicals seep into our drinking water; the cowboys are ruling the range; and our small and densely populated island fills up with toxic rubbish.

5

THE AGE OF CONSENTS

*Industrial pollution of the water
environment*

The water authorities and industry are involved in a giant chemistry
experiment using the environment as a test tube.

Tim Birch, Greenpeace, 1988

Any industry, from a dark satanic mill to a sophisticated
pharmaceutical company, produces waste by-products.
Whether gas, liquid or solid, these have to be disposed of. A
proportion goes into the poorly regulated hazardous-waste
business we discussed in the previous chapter; other waste is
pumped either straight into rivers or into water-authority
sewers. Flowing water has in the past been regarded as a great
purifier, able to dilute and render harmless almost anything
thrown into it. But all water is susceptible to pollution. Groundwater, from which we draw much of our drinking supplies, is
especially so.

Industry pollutes both by accident and by design. Accidental
spillages are one thing, but water is also contaminated by
chemicals that factories are allowed to discharge perfectly
legally. By law factories are subject to discharge consents
agreed with the local water authority. These are supposed to
regulate the composition and the quantity of the discharge.
What we don't know is how far companies comply with these
consents. We do know, however, that in 1988 there were
23,000 reported pollution incidents in Britain, double the figure
for 1982, and that industry was responsible for 37 per cent of
them.[1] We also know that during the 1980s more and more
rivers have been classed as unable to support life – almost
4,500 kilometres of river by 1988.

When the Control of Pollution Act was being formulated in
the 1970s, 'A lot of industries said they couldn't allow details

of their discharges to be made public because it would reveal their processes to competitors,' according to Andrew Lees of Friends of the Earth. 'So when industrial discharges take place into sewers, the law protects the supposed commercial interests of the companies and deprives the public of any means of finding out what is going on.' The fact that senior industrialists often sit on the boards of the water authorities cannot exactly encourage them to get tough on industrial pollution. Some board members are polluters, or former polluters, themselves.

When discharges are made directly into rivers the law states that some information must be made available. There are public registers at the regional headquarters of the water authorities. These may be non-specific, however, and often do not give details of exactly what is being discharged. Even this limited information is not collated nationally. We have no national picture of how industry is performing in terms of protecting the environment.

Friends of the Earth has investigated industrial-discharge consents in Yorkshire. It found some to be pretty woolly. One consent states that the company is permitted to discharge 'the effluent from chemical manufacturing', which certainly seems a little vague. Tim Birch of Greenpeace told us that some discharge consents were granted not with regard to pollution control but on the basis of what industry could comply with. The Control of Pollution Act (COPA) was formulated to prevent pollution, but, according to Tim Birch, 'Industry has used COPA as a smokescreen.' In the Mersey area one group of chemicals discharged into the water is the halogenated hydrocarbons. You couldn't devise a worse chemical than a halogenated hydrocarbon. They are synthetic, persistent and accumulative, and they can react in the environment to form other chemicals. From laboratory tests it is known that these chemicals are teratogenic (that is, they cause birth defects) in animals. Industrial discharges can kill whole river systems. The Humber began receiving industrial pollution in the late 1940s. By the early 1950s there had been a dramatic reduction in the local catch of sole, cod and shrimp. Within the decade the whole inshore fishing fleet had disappeared.

Water authorities are very reluctant to give detailed information about non-compliance with industrial-discharge consents. Environmentalists have to do their own monitoring to find out what individual companies are up to. The company concerned is not obliged to show that what it is doing is safe; voluntarily funded organizations must demonstrate otherwise. When environmentalists take samples they sometimes find chemicals in the water that no one even suspected were there. Tests carried out in Widnes revealed chemicals, including halogenated hydrocarbons, for which no consents had ever been issued and of which the water authority was apparently blissfully unaware. The problem is that water authorities know that they should test for certain chemicals in the water only if they are told what is being discharged. A company can pull the wool over the eyes of even the most diligent water authority.

So much for the 'planned' industrial pollution of water-authority consents. Pollution comes from accidents too. Until recently the city of Norwich was particularly vulnerable to water pollution. The whole city, about 180,000 people, was then supplied from a single water intake on the river Wensum. One kilometre upstream is the May and Baker chemical factory; between the intake and the factory is a bridge used by tankers carrying chemicals. An accident at the factory or on the bridge could have contaminated the city's entire water supply. The water authority needed an alternative water source and selected the groundwater in an area called Costessey Pits, not far from May and Baker's factory. But there were problems. Both soil and water near the factory were found to be contaminated with poisonous chemicals. One lagoon contained 300 times as much mercury as normal soil and was full of dead trees and bare mud. As for the underground water, it was found to be contaminated with bromide, sulphate, benzene, toluene and other chemicals. A public inquiry was held in May 1984 at which it was stated that the source of the groundwater pollution was the May and Baker chemical factory. One of the scientists from Anglian Water's Norwich division, giving evidence at the inquiry, said, 'A number of spillages, pollution incidents and surface-water contamination problems have occurred ...

Contamination on this site is unavoidable in spite of the recognized efforts made by the company and of the frequent visits and inspections made by officers of the water authority.' The company said that it had done nothing illegal and was trying to clean up the mess. It has now changed its name to Rhône-Poulenc (that of its French parent company) in the interests of corporate identity. Norwich still gets all its water from the Wensum, although the intake has had to be moved to a point upstream of the factory. Friends of the Earth claims that the company 'effectively destroyed a valuable public resource'.

The problem is that pollution doesn't go away. Yesterday's industrial discharge has a nasty habit of turning up in tomorrow's teacups. Throughout the country there have been a number of occasions on which a water authority or water company has examined a sample taken from one of its groundwater boreholes and has been amazed and horrified to discover that the water is polluted with industrial chemicals. In June 1988 the Lea Valley water company announced that three of its drinking-water sources were contaminated by chlorinated solvents. The sources serve 150,000 people in Luton and Dunstable. Water in one area contained trichloroethylene at concentrations four times the World Health Organization's guideline standard. Yet nobody knows where the pollution came from. Something similar happened in Andover in 1988, when a consumer complained about the funny taste of her water. Southern Water found that a spillage of over 450 litres of chlorinated solvents had contaminated a borehole. The water authority told us that EEC drinking-water limits had not been exceeded in this case but that it had had to install a special water-treatment machine and that it was pumping out the pollutant at a cost of £15,000.

Chlorinated solvents are used for paper making, metal plating and electrical engineering and as degreasers in drycleaning. The chemicals can leak from storage tanks and seep down into groundwater. They can then migrate, sometimes by hundreds or thousands of metres. This is why they sometimes turn up unexpectedly in drinking-water supplies before the original pollution incident is even noticed. The good news is that this happens only if there is a porous underground system subject to geological cracking; the bad news is that this describes the geology of almost all Britain's main underground reservoirs. Seeping through these underground fissures, pollution can affect an enormous area. The British Geological Survey warned in a 1987 report on solvents and pesticides, 'Even a small spill of a few litres in volume could, in theory, contaminate many millions of litres of groundwater.'

Until these solvents started turning up in underground aquifers, it was assumed that spilled chemicals would just evaporate. Unfortunately, they are not got rid of so easily. These chemicals are very persistent, some taking decades to break down. Once chemicals have contaminated groundwater supplies, clean-up operations are very difficult and very expensive. A river constantly renews itself: the water flows out to the sea and is replaced by water coming down off the hills. The whole river system is permanently being flushed out. With groundwater, however, the flushing takes a lot longer, as the water moves far more slowly. Pollution can take decades to disappear. The British Geological Survey report says that if large volumes of solvents get into the groundwater, it can result in an 'environmental disaster'. Such disasters may well be under way already. It has been estimated that 10 per cent of Britain's aquifers contain concentrations of solvents at above the level recommended by the World Health Organization.

As with pesticides, we know little about the effects of industrial chemicals in our drinking water. If you go to your doctor with a complaint, he or she is unlikely to turn around and say, 'Ah, trichloroethylene in the water.' Yet industrial solvents are well-known carcinogens. The Water Research Council is concerned about exposure to such chemicals, and reported in 1981, 'There is evidence ... to indicate that repeated small doses of some organic chemicals may lead to chronic toxic effects.'

Industrial contamination threatens many groundwater sources. Bob Harris of Severn Trent says, 'In urban areas, industrial solvents are widely found in groundwater.' He told us that it was difficult to deal with such diffuse pollutants. It is easy to understand why: the source may be untraceable, and clean-up operations may be virtually impossible. Even if the source can be traced, the water authority may not get much joy out of claiming compensation. In 1981 a routine sample of water in Suffolk revealed the presence of solvents in an aquifer that supplied water to 40,000 people. The source of the pollution was traced to the US Air Force base at RAF Mildenhall, and a major public-supply borehole had to be closed. Anglian Water's claim for compensation was refused because the airfield has Crown immunity.

Accidents can happen to anyone. With the best will in the world, pollution can slip into rivers unnoticed. In early 1985 a fractured underground pipeline from the Monsanto chemical works at Ruabon in north Wales caused a purple liquid to seep into the river. As it was underground, the fracture went unnoticed for eleven days, while everyone wondered where the pollution was coming from. In November 1988 another pipeline fracture occurred at the Monsanto works. A cocktail of chemicals that should have been treated went straight into the river instead. This time the problem was noticed immediately, and Monsanto informed the water authority, which closed all four abstraction points until the pollution had passed. In this case both the company and the water authority acted quickly. But what about those companies that do not act so responsibly? What about those who regularly pollute and don't bother to tell anyone about it?

The worst kind of pollution occurs when a company pollutes the water above an abstraction point and doesn't notice, and the water authority also fails to notice the pollution until it's too late. Such an incident happened on the river Dee a few years ago. From Thursday, 26 January 1984, 2 million people in Wales and the north-west of England were severely affected by high levels of phenol in water from the river, caused by a single slug of pollution from an industrial site on the Dee. A plastics company later paid £22,000 compensation to the water authorities in an out-of-court settlement, although it refused to accept responsibility for the incident.

The worst part of the whole affair was that nobody noticed that anything was wrong until complaints started flooding in from the public. The water authorities and water companies involved assumed that pollution would be detected by workers before it got into the distribution system. They were wrong about this. It wasn't until switchboards were jammed with complaints that the scale of the problem was realized. Restaurateurs were in despair. Production at a food factory was halted. Water authorities advised pregnant women and mothers of bottle-fed babies to use bottled water, which naturally meant that, within hours, there was not a drop of Evian to be had in the whole of Merseyside. The Royal Liverpool Hospital, needing supplies for a kidney dialysis unit, asked the fire service to pump fresh water from a tank at the Cammell Laird shipyard.

Whenever there is an accident involving a possible risk to health, whether it is associated with water, chemicals or nuclear power, an official will seek to reassure us that everything is under control and that there is no need to panic. In this case spokespeople claimed first that, because of melting snow, extra chlorine had been added to the water and that this was the reason for the peculiar taste. Throughout the weekend, as people wondered why their tea tasted of TCP, the official advice was that the contaminated supplies represented no threat to health.

Dr John Ashton of Liverpool University disagrees. He points out that the pollution occurred on Monday, two days before it was noticed. Medical advice was not sought until Friday. 'Reliable information on the extent to which levels such as these pose a threat to people's health seems to be lacking.' The phenol may have reacted with the chlorine used in water treatment, for example, to produce new substances more toxic than the phenol itself. A second substance present in the water, 2 ethyl hexanol, was not identified until more than a week after the event. As for effects on health, the Communicable Disease Surveillance Centre at Colindale found there was a 'very great increase in the occurrence of gastro-intestinal illness among those living in the affected areas'.

Since the phenol incident, the amount of monitoring done on the river has been increased in frequency and sophistication.

The Dee is now very highly controlled and regulated. But why were the authorities unprepared in the first place? As with the more recent and more serious pollution incident at Camelford, Cornwall, which we discuss in a later chapter, nobody thought of the possibility of an accident until it actually happened. Serious pollution incidents like this make the headlines. Smaller spills, causing fish deaths but perhaps no obvious human ill-health, tend to slip by unnoticed. Yet they all contribute to the cocktail of chemicals in our water.

Industrial pollution has been with us for a long time. But its nature has changed. The rivers used to be dirty because of sewage and soot, which were highly visible. We now live in a new era of neglect. The chemicals in our rivers are often insidious: they are invisible. The water may smell odd because of chemical contamination, but otherwise the only indication we get that something is wrong is when the fish start dying – if there were fish there in the first place. Tim Birch says, 'I saw kids jumping into the Mersey downstream of the ICI Paraquat plant. Those children might easily swallow some of the water; even if they don't, some chemicals can pass through the skin. Because we can't see the pollution, we often have no idea that it is there, and that is highly dangerous.'

Her Majesty's Inspectorate of Pollution is intended to monitor pollution from industry and has powers to reduce emissions. However, two senior members of the Inspectorate have recently resigned, and morale among their former colleagues is very low. Understaffed and under-resourced, inspectors calculate that they will be able to visit some factories only once every twenty-five years. They are supposed to visit once every five years. In 1988 in England and Wales there were nearly 9,000 recorded industrial pollution incidents but only ninety-eight prosecutions, a rate of less than 2 per cent.[2] Why aren't the polluters prosecuted more often? 'The reality is that water authorities are understaffed,' according to Andrew Lees of Friends of the Earth. 'If you're going to mount a prosecution, it's very expensive because, obviously, you have to get good independent analytical data; you need to put a lot of people on to the case; you need to bring in water-pollution experts, chemists, the legal department. Then you end up going to court – that's expensive in itself. At the end of it the company might get fined a few thousand pounds, meanwhile all those resources could have been used for something else. From the water authority's point of view, if you've got one leg nailed to the ground, you know it's not worth entering marathons.'

It is possible, in a charitable moment, to understand why some farmers complain of being victimized over water pollution. The Water Authorities Association produces a glossy booklet on pollution by farm waste every year, in which it details incidents, complains about the level of fines and, quite rightly, draws the public's attention to the rising tide of rural pollution. No such booklet is produced on pollution by industrial waste, though industry causes twice as many pollution incidents as does agriculture. When we asked why this was so, we were told by one official, 'Farm-waste pollution is more in the public eye.' Perhaps few people feel that it is in their interests to publicize the pollution record of powerful companies.

The new National Rivers Authority (NRA) will have its work cut out if it is to arrest this alarming trend. In the privatized water industry of the future the NRA will be doing much the same job as water authorities do at present. The system of discharge consents will stand, as will the secrecy that surrounds them. Sampling techniques are unlikely to improve. It remains to be seen whether the government will allocate sufficient resources to the NRA to ensure that the people who police our pollution standards no longer have one leg nailed to the ground.

6

MOVING THE GOALPOSTS
Illegal sewage pollution of rivers and estuaries

The legislation we have at the moment, wherever possible, seems to be used to authorize pollution, not prevent pollution.
Andrew Lees, Friends of the Earth, 1989

For many years people have been concerned that drinking water is sometimes drawn from rivers downstream from a sewage outfall pipe, a practice known as 'water re-use'. It doesn't sound very nice, but it's not generally thought to be bad for us provided the sewage-treatment works is functioning properly and provided there's not too much industrial waste in the effluent.

As we have seen, industry has been encouraged to tie itself into the sewage system. In theory this should make industrial waste more manageable. However, many of our sewage-treatment works may simply not be up to the job of dealing with industrial effluent effectively. The problem is that our sewage system is very old. Much of it dates from the nineteenth century, yet today it struggles to cope with pollution and waste that is very much the product of the twentieth.

Water authorities are currently in a difficult position. As the guardians of our rivers and drinking water resources they are responsible for monitoring pollution and ensuring that water is safe to drink. If necessary, they are expected to use the law against individuals and companies responsible for the pollution of rivers and watercourses. However, the water authorities also run sewage-treatment plants that discharge into rivers and streams, making them potential polluters as well; thus they are both poachers and gamekeepers. To ensure that they carry out both duties properly, there is the system of consents – agreed limits that certain substances in sewage outfall are not allowed to exceed. A sewage-treatment works is supposed to comply with its consent or face prosecution under the Control of Pollution Act. The record on compliance with these consents is very poor. About one in five sewage works does not comply fully.[1] Some areas of the country are worse than others: in the Thames area it's more like one in three that fails to comply. We're talking here about breaking the law. We are also talking about dangerous chemicals passing through sewage-treatment plants into rivers and, possibly, into the public water supply.

A sewage-treatment works will certainly reduce the organic load of waste matter, killing some of the bacteria in human waste and protecting water from becoming de-oxygenated. Nevertheless, if a sewage works receives certain kinds of industrial effluent, all that takes place is a relocation of the pollution. Some is bound up in sewage sludge, which may be dumped in the sea or spread on the land; the rest is dispersed in the effluent discharged into the river. Industrial waste products such as heavy metals and persistent pesticides may become slightly diluted, but they do not disappear. In fact, they accumulate in the food chain. Worms, for example, may store them in their bodies; if the worms are eaten by eels, the poison passes on to them and builds up again; if the eels are eaten by herons, the poison may be too much for them and they may die.

Some very dangerous chemicals find their way through sewage works and into our rivers. In April 1987 there was a mercury scare in the river Yare: mercury found in river-bed sediment was between two and thirty times greater than normal background levels, according to a report by Anglian Water. The amount of mercury was especially high downstream from the Whitlingham sewage works. Eels that lived in the water there were subjected to a health warning from the Ministry of Agriculture. The chairman of Norwich Council's environmental health committee said that the mercury deposits 'need give no concern over the safety of the public water supply' because they were downstream from the supply intake point. Yet, according to Neil Ward of the Robens Institute, mercury from industrial sources can be very dangerous. In Japan it caused forty-one deaths after contaminated fish and shellfish were eaten. Horrific deformities in new-born children were also ascribed to the mercury poisoning.

Over a fifth of all recorded pollution incidents in Britain are related to water-authority sewage treatment. The problem is not new. In 1974 some 64 per cent of the main sewage works in England and Wales failed to meet standards set by the government for their discharges. Ten years later nothing had changed, and 64 per cent were still failing. But in late 1984 an apparently miraculous event occurred. Suddenly hardly any sewage works failed to meet the standards. Those familiar with the government's traditional approach to environmental problems will not be surprised to learn that this instant improvement was nothing to do with massive capital expenditure; it came about because the government changed the rules and relaxed the standards. (Whitehall insiders call this technique 'moving the goalposts'.) Despite this manipulation of statistics in 1984, by 1988 almost 23 per cent of the main sewage-treatment works in England and Wales still failed to meet the legal standards then in force. This failure amounted to a criminal offence under the Control of Pollution Act. Most sewage works are already allowed to break their consents up to 5 per cent of the time without having to worry. If this loophole no longer applied, it has been estimated that almost 80 per cent of British sewage works would be officially illegal.[2]

Pollution consents are often calculated on the basis not of a high river-water standard, as you might expect, but of what is possible to achieve without spending too much money. The Anglian Water Authority's 1986 plan said that 'discharge consents approved by the Department of the Environment reflect [sewage] works' capability', not any notion of what might be good for the river. It also states that the need to avoid prosecution under the Control of Pollution Act has 'changed the emphasis away from the achievement of river-water quality objectives to treatment-works compliance'. Thus we now have a bizarre situation in which the risk of prosecution has stimulated a lowering, not a raising, of standards by sending the water authorities scrambling to have their standards lowered – another case of moving the goalposts. The House of Commons

Environmental Committee says that this is 'not an acceptable state of affairs'. In a recent report it commented, 'Apart from the threat to water quality, it places water authorities in a weak position when they themselves should be taking firm action against other polluters.' Andrew Lees of Friends of the Earth is scathing: 'The legislation we have at the moment, wherever possible, seems to be used to authorize pollution, not prevent pollution.'

New Scientist magazine carried out an investigation into effluent from Mersey Basin sewage works in November 1988. The magazine looked at biological oxygen demand – the amount of oxygen taken up by micro-organisms in the sewage as waste in the water decays. In 1978 Swinton sewage works had an effluent consent that allowed a BOD of 20 milligrams per litre. By 1988 the amount permitted was 75 milligrams per litre. The goalposts hadn't just been moved: they'd been stretched halfway to the corner flag! *New Scientist* found other neat tricks too. In 1978 North West Water took 200 to 300 samples a year from large sewage works. At that time the sewage works had to remain within the scope of their consents 95 per cent of the time: they were allowed to fail on only 5 per cent of their samples. Now the water authority takes about fifty samples a year. With this level of monitoring a sewage works is allowed to fail its consent up to five times, or 10 per cent of the current sampling. Thus the 'acceptable failure rate' has been doubled. *New Scientist* also reported that sewage works serving half of Yorkshire Water Authority's customers fail their consents – and this despite the relaxations in standards and general goalpost-adjusting that was intended to make all sewage works legal.

Overall the Mersey Basin is a grim example of declining water standards. Researchers consider the area to be one of the most polluted in western Europe. In 1982 government minister Michael Heseltine called the estuary 'the open sewer of the north-west . . . an affront to the standards people rightly expect in the second half of the twentieth century . . . If we fail to respond, we shall pass on to later generations a devastating indictment of our will and energy to improve our environment '

In the late 1980s the situation is, if anything, worse: 1,224 kilometres of the Mersey river system are now classed as too polluted to sustain fish life, 340 kilometres more than in 1982. Over half of the area's sewage works provide samples that are dirtier than those taken ten years ago. Some Mersey Basin sewage works are now officially allowed to discharge 50 per cent more pollution than they were ten years ago, and one, at Halewood, is allowed to dump raw sewage straight into the river. Greenpeace scientists have found 200 chemicals in the effluent there. It is indeed a devastating indictment of our will and energy to improve the environment.

Concerned organizations are now taking water authorities to court over their sewage discharges. The Anglers Co-operative Association prosecuted Thames Water over effluent from Aylesbury sewage works, which contained high levels of ammonia between September 1986 and January 1987. The water authority was fined £1,000 on each of six charges and ordered to pay costs. In 1988 Derbyshire County Council became the first local authority to take its water authority to court over pollution, claiming that North West Water broke its own rules about how much effluent should be discharged from sewage works at Whaley Bridge into the river Goyt. The water authority was fined £1,500 for polluting the Goyt with sewage effluent that contained industrial waste. But North West Water managed to get away with discharging some sewage that was twenty times the legal limit because the case was discovered too late to be brought to court. The water authority had not registered the test results until long after the incident occurred. Normally the results of laboratory analysis are entered within twenty-eight days; this time it took four months. The sewage-pollution tests conducted and reported by North West Water itself are the only evidence that can legally be used against the water authority.

North West Water has complained that Derbyshire County Council is putting it in an impossible position. If the water authority wants to avoid another court action, its sewage works must not accept too much industrial waste. The waste that it cannot accept is therefore left untreated and runs straight into the river. Result: the river is even more polluted now than when the authority was breaking the sewage consent. Whichever way the authority moves, the environment suffers. Such are the dilemmas of our antique sewage system.

The government has promised capital expenditure of £700 million to help bring sewage works up to legal standards by 1992. But this promise has been greeted with scepticism by water-authority officials. They say that they haven't been asked what such a programme would cost and fear that £700 million will not be enough. The entire privatization programme could be threatened by this problem. The possible prosecution of water authorities for breaching their consents could be a serious deterrent to investors. Going to the marketplace with organizations knowingly engaged in illegality could well be a significant obstacle to a successful flotation. The government could eliminate the right to prosecute, but that move would be politically sensitive. More likely is a further relaxation of consents, for an interim period, for those sewage works that are unable to meet current standards.

Andrew Lees, for one, expects the worst: 'There is now a very strong likelihood that the government will move the goalposts again to protect the water authorities from prosecution before, and immediately following, water privatization. There are two reasons for that: first, because it's going to be very difficult for the government to persuade a reputable businessman to walk out of his gentlemen's club and into court to get stuck with a criminal record; second, criminal liabilities would blemish the prospectuses that the government needs to persuade the City that it's worth buying into privatized water companies.' In fact, there have already been newspaper reports that the government plans to do just this. According to these stories, the Department of the Environment has invited the water authorities to apply to have their pollution standards relaxed yet again in the months before privatization. This would get the government off the hook and would mean that it would not have to offer for sale companies that regularly break the law. As the water environment deteriorates around us, Whitehall resounds, once again, to the unmistakable sound of goalposts on the move.

River classifications

As we have seen in this and other chapters, Britain's rivers are getting dirtier. Pollution from industry, farms and the water authorities' own sewage-treatment works is pouring into them in ever-increasing quantities. The number of pollution incidents increases yearly; river quality, as measured by the official classification system, is deteriorating.

Rivers are classified in five categories: 1A, 1B, 2, 3 and 4. The first three classes are able to support fish; classes 3 and 4 can't. When the Control of Pollution Act was passed in 1974, it was hoped that all rivers would eventually be improved so they would be able to support fish. That hasn't happened. On the contrary, in the years 1980–85 overall river quality, as measured by these categories, deteriorated. Since then rivers have declined even further. Moreover, no account has been taken of river-quality reduction within each class: a river can decline from being a 'good' class 2 to a 'bad' class 2, and this reduction in quality will go unrecorded. Nor are all rivers classified: Andrew Lees says, 'At the moment 35 per cent of the main river length in England and Wales is not monitored on a routine basis for river quality. If the existing river-classification system was applied to all rivers, we believe there would be an indication of a massive decline in river quality.'

Despite the Control of Pollution Act water authorities have been powerless to stem the flow of pollution. Lack of cash is widely blamed for their impotence. Budgets have been limited by the government's Performance Aims Regime, imposed in 1983, which was intended to make the water authorities more self-sufficient in financial terms. But you can't keep up standards, let alone improve them, without money.

7

GOING THROUGH THE MOTIONS

Sewage pollution of sea water and beaches

By wounding nature we wound ourselves above all.
Jacques Cousteau, 1987

If you have ever had diarrhoea while on holiday, you probably put it down to the food. But instead of something you ate, the cause could have been something you drank: particles of untreated sewage floating in the sea water.

In the summer of 1988 we took the family to Somerset. One day we visited Minehead to let our children play on the beach. At the water's edge we quickly changed our minds. The sea was full of tiny scraps of tissue: white, pink, blue, all the colours of domestic toilet paper. (Apparently it has since been cleaned up.) We found it hard to believe that the authorities would allow bathing in sewage-polluted seawater at all, but a little research proved that many of Britain's bathing beaches are conveniently situated near local sewage outfall pipes.

Everything we put down a toilet can wash up on a beach. A survey of holidaymakers carried out by Greenpeace and the Robens Institute in 1987 found that people had recently spotted lumps of human excrement, sanitary towels and used condoms floating in the water. (We suppose pollutant-spotting makes a change from traditional seaside pursuits like searching for crabs and driftwood.) The statistics make gloomy reading for enthusiastic bathers. According to an EEC survey in 1986, 94 per cent of Dutch beaches conformed to the European standards for sewage pollution, as did 86 per cent of French beaches, 81 per cent of Italian and 85 per cent of Irish. Britain had the very worst record in Europe: a miserable 44 per cent of our bathing beaches came up to scratch.* Maybe it is because government ministers tend to take their families to foreign beaches that this scandalous situation is allowed to continue. Certainly we British don't seem to get very upset about bathing in our own sewage. In the words of an old joke, 'It's not so much like swimming round here, it's more like going through the motions!'

The British have an island mentality: we tend to assume the sea can cope with everything we throw into it. More than 400 sewage outfalls are situated near coastal waters, and 227 of them dump sewage that is untreated. The waste of approximately 7 million people is processed through coastal sewage disposal – though the word 'processed' is perhaps inappropriate because much of the waste is simply strained through sieves and poured, untreated, out of pipes and into the sea. Some systems are more sophisticated, treating the sewage to remove certain bacteria before piping it out to sea.

Far more disease may be associated with coastal bathing than we realize. In the 1970s the United States Environmental Protection Agency carried out an extensive study to determine if there was any link between swimming in polluted water and illness. They found that stomach complaints were associated with swimming on polluted beaches, and that children under ten were most prone to them. Holidaymakers were found to be more at risk than local people. The Greenpeace/Robens study concluded: 'Bathers who immersed their heads in sea-water polluted by sewage were significantly more likely to complain of gastro-intestinal symptoms than those who did not immerse their heads or who bathed at a non-polluted resort.'

Scientist Pat Gowan was recently commissioned by an E E C environmental agency to examine Britain's dirty beaches. He believes that there is a serious health risk associated with bathing in sewage-polluted sea water. He even warns about those healthy walks along the prom. If the sea water is polluted, you may pick up dangerous organisms through inhaling sea spray. He told us, 'Thousands of people get ill on their holidays and put it down to food or alcohol. In fact, these people are

* See appendix, 'The polluted-beach league', page 119.

often ill because of sewage in the water. I would advise holiday-makers to pick their resort very carefully. Apart from serious gastro-intestinal problems, there is hepatitis, polio and even meningitis in some sea water. If you really want to swim, then visit the local chlorinated pool – that is my advice.'

Sewage pollution is usually measured in faecal coli (bacteria) per 100 millilitres of water (f.c./100 ml). American scientists estimate that when pollution measures 200 f.c./100 ml, fifteen out of every 1,000 bathers can be expected to fall ill. The present EEC limit for sea water is 2,000 f.c./100 ml, which would imply, according to the American data, that out of every 1,000 swimmers 150 people will fall ill. Some of this illness is not serious, but diseases linked with swimming in polluted sea water include diarrhoea, infections of the ears, eyes, nose and throat, hepatitis, enteritis and cystitis. If you are unvaccinated, you even run the risk of catching polio and typhoid.

It can also be dangerous to eat shellfish that have come straight from feeding beds near sewage outfall pipes. Their feeding involves the filtration of many litres of water every day, and they pass on any bacteria and viruses in the water to whatever eats them. This is why some shellfish in Britain now have to be purified for a while in clean water before being sold for human consumption.

The EEC has come up with a standard to aim for. In the mid-1970s a directive was introduced ruling that designated bathing beaches had to be monitored to ensure that they met certain bacteriological and virological standards. How many beaches did this island nation designate as commonly used for public bathing? Just twenty-seven: fewer than the number of beaches declared by landlocked Luxembourg. And they did not include such famous resorts as Brighton, Blackpool and Eastbourne. After many complaints the number of designated bathing beaches was finally increased in 1986: nearly 400 beaches are registered now and should, in theory, meet the EEC health standard. In practice over one third still do not. These included, in 1988, such popular resorts as Blackpool, parts of Weston-super-Mare, Lyme Regis, parts of Great Yarmouth, Morecambe and Broadstairs. The great majority of water authorities do not post their test results for public inspection. Consequently most holidaymakers have no idea where the sewage outfalls are or whether a particular beach meets the EEC standard for bathing water.

It is not as if the EEC limits were particularly strict. Greenpeace recently took a number of British beaches and tested them against the safety limits of various countries: 37 per cent of the beaches met EEC standards; 18.5 per cent met current American standards; and only 11 per cent met the strict Canadian standards. Some beaches were better than others: Whitstable in Kent and Fistral and Towan in Cornwall met even the Canadian standards. Bournemouth and Weymouth conformed to European standards. But others can be very poor. Blackpool has at times broken the EEC mandatory limit for faecal streptococci ten times over. It became so bad there that in 1987 Greenpeace activists attempted to post warning signs on Blackpool beach, much to the dismay of local traders, who rushed into the water to demonstrate its safety.

In July 1987 the EEC complained to the British government about the bathing water at Southport, Merseyside, which was 'not of the quality required', according to the European officials. A similar complaint has also been made about water at Blackpool. Environmental health officers in Thurrock warned in the summer of 1988 that people should not paddle or swim off local beaches because of sewage pollution. Torbay, on Britain's south-west 'riviera', is thought to be among the best and cleanest beaches in the country, yet there is a raw sewage outfall only a short distance away, pouring thousands of litres of excrement into the sea every day. Torbay regularly wins awards for its beach, which must say something about our national standards for bathing water. In 1984 a local newspaper in the south-west published a letter from six doctors claiming that hepatitis was evident at the Porthmeor and Porthminster beaches. The doctors said that human excrement was regularly washed up on the shoreline. At that time holidaymakers were advised to protect themselves with polio and typhoid inoculations before visiting the areas. This is the sort of advice people associate with travel to the Third World, not to Cornwall, although we now understand these two beaches have been cleaned up.

Sea water is thought to disperse and destroy the harmful bacteria in sewage. Raw sewage is screened in the attempt to remove plastics and other solids that cannot readily be broken up by the sea. Since 1959 the authorities have said, 'Bathing in sewage-polluted sea water carries only a negligible risk to health, even on beaches that are aesthetically very unsatisfactory.' Until the EEC directive was applied in 1976, it was felt that there was no need for quality standards for recreational waters so long as there was no visible evidence of sewage solids.

New and controversial research from the United States has led some experts to question this view, however. Jay Grimes, a research associate professor of microbiology at the University of Maryland, has provided evidence that pathogens survive longer in sea water than was originally thought. It was formerly assumed that pathogenic bacteria (those that harm human beings) died off in the sea very quickly. This assumption was based on experiments in which scientists took samples of sea water and tried to grow bacteria from them. If they could not cultivate bacteria, the scientists reasonably concluded that there was none in the sample. But Professor Grimes's experiments suggest that the bacteria are in the water after all, though in a different state. He calls the bacteria 'viable, but non-culturable' – that is, in a state of dormancy.

Professor Grimes believes that pathogens from sewage survive in this dormant state and continue to pose a threat to human health. He criticizes the old method of testing for their presence in sea water: 'The use of conventional, selective media to examine marine waters, shellfish and shellfish beds for faecal coliforms and E. coli will yield misleading results.' The bacteria cannot be grown on a laboratory plate, but when they find a suitable environment, such as a human intestine, they become active again and cause illness such as diarrhoea and skin rashes. An example is the salmonella enteriditis bacteria and *Vibrio cholerae*, which causes cholera. Viruses are also present in sewage discharges. Viruses cause a variety of diseases and are believed to trigger certain cancers. They are known to be long-lived and may be present even though they are un-detected by conventional tests. His research has led Professor Grimes to conclude: 'Disposal of pathogen-containing wastes in coastal waters is an alternative that should not be given serious consideration on account of danger to human health.' The new research has caused Greenpeace to argue: 'The EEC should now review both the health considerations on which microbiological standards of bathing-water quality in Europe are based and the monitoring regimes which are intended to enforce them.'

In the Yorkshire resort of Scarborough there is bitter con-troversy about water-authority plans to replace a short sewage pipe with a longer one. At other locations where longer pipes have been constructed there has been a marked improvement in the bacteriological quality of the waters. Ian Crease, the north-eastern divisional operations manager for the Yorkshire Water Authority, has told the local paper: 'There is no threat to sea life in our scheme, in which sewage will be deposited 1,450 metres from the sea wall.'

This sounds reasonable enough, but the proposition is being opposed by a group called the Sons of Neptune. They sound like a pagan cult, but they are, in fact, middle-aged professional men: a solicitor, a chiropodist, a chartered accountant, a market-ing executive, a schoolmaster, a former sea captain and a bookmaker. The Sons of Neptune oppose the scheme partly because they say it does not take proper account of the new research by Professor Grimes and others, and partly because they believe that sewage will be washed back on to the shore. The Sons carry out inspired publicity stunts – for example, dressing up as funeral directors and collecting 'bodies' from the beach – to demonstrate what might happen if the new outfall is built. They have also dressed somebody up as Dracula (on the slim pretext that Bram Stoker wrote *Dracula* in nearby Whitby), who chased children dressed in Victorian clothes. He had the name of the water authority on his back. Such activities have not endeared them to the officials of Yorkshire Water, who are convinced that their scheme is quite safe.

The Scarborough campaigners are not opposed to long sea

outfalls as such, but they are pressing for an alternative site and for the disinfecting of waste prior to dumping. They point out that the pipe will be only about 1 kilometre from the shore at low tide. They have already made one formal complaint to the EEC, alleging that the present EEC safety standards for bathing water are outdated and fail to give adequate protection against disease. In support of their case the Sons of Neptune cited an affidavit from Professor Grimes. The Sons also commissioned a report from Bruce Denness, former Professor of Ocean Engineering at Newcastle University. Denness argues that the new outfall would allow a substantial amount of sewage to wash on to the beaches. The water authority disputes this and claims that its research shows otherwise. Denness also discusses the whole policy of pouring untreated sewage directly into the sea, concluding: 'Sewage which has been subjected only to primary treatment [i.e. sieving and mashing] should not be released to the marine environment, as the absence of any disinfection process will lead to an accumulation of pathogens with potentially disastrous consequences.'

In many resorts the beach is the main tourist attraction. So if the beach is dirty, you would expect local people and the local council to be furious. Occasionally they have been: Southend beach has recently been the focus of fierce controversy. Until 1988 sewage was poured into the sea along short outfall pipes, from which it often turned round and came straight back to land. In the summer of that year this system was replaced by a long outfall pipe, which took the sewage further out to sea. But during the changeover period there were problems, and the water became excessively polluted. We were told by the local council that bacteria were found at levels 100 times higher than the EEC guideline standard. The council asked that the beach be closed to the public or else posted with warning signs to holidaymakers about the dangers of swimming. Apparently there was 'massive resistance' to these measures, and the beach stayed open. One boy who went swimming in the polluted water became very ill shortly afterwards with a virus infection. His family took bottles of Southend sea water to the door of No. 10 Downing Street to protest about his case. Six months later, and with the new pipe operational, the beach was certainly cleaner but still not clean enough, said the local council. It claimed that because the sewage was only screened, not treated, before it was dumped in the sea, levels of salmonella and coliform bacteria in the water were still high. The council is putting pressure on the water authority to install a full treatment works.

In other resorts secrecy is seen as the answer to dirty beaches. Some towns, such as Barrow-in-Furness, are quite open about pollution-test results because they have nothing to hide: their beaches are fairly clean. Others hush up bad results because of their potentially devastating effect on the local economy. If the secret does leak out, a council may well engage in a public relations stunt to reassure potential tourists: getting the mayor to take a dip with a local beauty queen, for instance. The attitude is often 'What they don't know won't hurt them'; local hoteliers and arcade owners are not best pleased when groups like the Sons of Neptune draw attention to the dangers of swimming in a sewage-polluted sea. 'They are not doing Scarborough any favours,' a local councillor told journalists, voicing a common feeling that it is the pressure group, not the pollution, that is the problem. Yet it is only when enough people know about the problem, and enough fuss is made, that anything is likely to be done about it.

If you are planning a holiday in Britain and would like to know what lies in store for you at your chosen resort, Dr Anne Scott of the Marine Conservation Society has written *The Good Beach Guide* to British holiday resorts. Published by Ebury Press, it gives details of water quality at 170 beaches and information about the amenities available in the resorts featured. The Marine Conservation Society also publishes a 'Golden List' of all the beaches in the country, giving the locations of nearby sewage outfall pipes and treatment works. Both publications are available from the Marine Conservation Society at 9, Gloucester Road, Ross-on-Wye, Hereford HR9 5BU, and they are invaluable if you want to avoid 'going through the motions' this summer.

We must at this point acknowledge the problems faced by

the water authorities, which do not have a bottomless purse. They have been reluctant to spend money on beaches when there is so much work to be done on improving the quality of drinking water and repairing ageing sewage works. South West Water has a particularly acute problem: it has a vast summer tourist population, which may well bring money into the area but also produces its share of sewage. South West Water is responsible for more beaches than any other water authority in England and Wales, yet the permanent population, which keeps the whole system functioning by paying the water rates, numbers only about 1.5 million.

The prognosis is not good. In November 1988 Nicholas Ridley, the Environment Secretary, told the House of Commons Environment Committee that the earliest possible date for cleaning up all Britain's beaches was 1995. It's important to remember that we're not talking just about tummy bugs. Sewage contains more than bacteria and viruses; it may also include industrial waste, such as mercury, that poisons sea life. In addition, the sea is the final repository for all the chemicals flowing down our polluted rivers. We have seen seals die, and we have seen an alarming increase in the number of deformed and mutated fish being pulled out of the North Sea. It should be enough to reiterate Jacques Cousteau's words about sea pollution: 'By wounding nature we wound ourselves above all.'

8

ACCIDENTS WILL HAPPEN
Poisoned tap water in Cornwall

. . . a major ecological disaster, the likes of which have not been
recorded in Britain before.

Dr Neil Ward, 1988

In the summer of 1988 an illness spread among the people of
north Cornwall. Lips and fingers felt strangely sticky. People
suffered from stomach pains, vomiting and diarrhoea. Others
found that their hair was turning green, their skin was itchy
and red and their joints were painful. Some passed blood in
their urine. Thousands were affected. These symptoms were
caused not by some modern plague but by poison. And the
source of that poison was the water supply.

This is a story of mishap and mismanagement, a story that
illustrates some of the worst aspects of modern water-authority
practice. A relief driver arrived at the Lowermoor treatment
works in Cornwall on Wednesday, 6 July, at 4.30 p.m. He had
a load of 20 tonnes of aluminium sulphate, the chemical used
to flocculate (purify) water. He was supposed to put his load
into a storage tank, but the site was unmanned. According to
the official report of the incident, 'Nobody was checking when
it was delivered, ensuring that the chemical was the right one
in the right quantity, ensuring that it was pumped into the
right place and signing off the delivery note.' The driver let
himself in with a key, which he shouldn't have had. He had no
map of the site but had been told the tank was on the left. The
'tank' was an unmarked aperture: 'To somebody unfamiliar
with the works it is the last place that he would expect to be a
receiving point for an important chemical,' says the report. He
found what he took to be the right opening. After all, his key
opened its cover. He deposited his load and left, his delivery
note unsigned.

Less than five hours later complaints started coming in to South West Water Authority about the water, which was curdling milk, tasting funny and making lips and fingers feel sticky. No one thought of the possibility of aluminium sulphate poisoning. The problem was presumed to be something to do with the lime pump, which normally adjusts the pH of the slightly acidic local water but had been giving a bit of trouble. It was not until nearly two days later, on the morning of Friday, 8 July, that someone noticed that the level in the aluminium sulphate tank was low. By then it was too late. 'Acidic water, with a high aluminium sulphate content, was working its way through the system,' according to the official report. No one knew how serious the pollution was. Staff began to panic and to flush water into rivers without consulting works operators or environmental protection staff. The death of tens of thousands of fish was the result.

Dr John Lawrence, the author of the official report, said of the pollution: 'The acid concerned is sulphuric, the strength of which depends on the concentration of aluminium sulphate.' Mention sulphuric acid and people start to think of chemistry lessons at school, of the teacher warning them not to touch it, maybe even demonstrating what it could do to a piece of cloth. You certainly wouldn't want to drink the stuff. Yet in July 1988, in the area around Camelford and Tintagel, 20,000 people were drinking water seriously contaminated with it.

One of those people was Mr Douglas Cross. Now retired, he has had twenty-five years' experience as a consultant ecologist. He is a water-pollution expert who has travelled all over the world lecturing on aquatic pollution and ecology. He is most unhappy with the way in which the incident was handled. For instance, it was not for several days after the contamination that the water authority knew the cause, yet it continued to reassure consumers that their water was harmless, even though it was foul-tasting and discoloured. The management of South West Water is, in Mr Cross's eyes, 'not fit to own a water authority'.

Dr Lawrence agrees that consumers were wrongly reassured: 'When the complaints of acidity were received it should have been clear from their nature that something was seriously wrong ... But the staff were confused; the only available explanation that they had was the lime-pump failure and that should not have been serious. Coupled with poor co-ordination within the authority, this was the reason that confusing and contradictory responses were given by different people ... No manager took charge ... and there seems to be a culture in which the public are told as little as possible and expected to trust the authority to look after their interests.' The original incident may have been due to unfortunate circumstances, but the response to it was clearly bad management. In some places bowsers were set up to provide an alternative water supply. Although this was a laudable attempt, it was not altogether successful. The bowsers were of different colours, and people didn't know what to look for; the bowsers came and went without warning; schools could not get a supply, while hotels could; some carried warnings to boil the water and some didn't. Confusion reigned supreme.

According to Douglas Cross, the water authority continued to give out nothing but reassuring noises for weeks. He says that the victims of the poisoning were not told what had happened even after 8 July, when the water authority knew the cause. It maintained that it was a lime-pump failure and told the health authority that there had been a 'slight acidity problem'. People affected were suspicious of this, particularly those who, like Mr Cross, knew something about water-treatment processes. 'There is no way the normal processes would produce this level of acidity,' he says. Because Mr Cross was not happy with the official line, he set up a local action group on a voluntary basis. It consisted of a small group of scientists, one GP and a few other concerned local people. Their aim was to gather information about what had been going on, since they feared that South West Water had not been entirely open about the cause of the pollution. Dr Richard Newman, a local GP, was one of those who felt that the consumers had been kept in the dark deliberately. He has called the information they were given a 'whitewash'. In particular, he says, little was said about the long-term health risks of the poisoning. It wasn't until members of the action group received an anonymous phone call from someone at South West Water on 21 July that they discovered the truth. Yet there was still no clear picture of what exactly had happened or of how much aluminium sulphate had got into the supply. The water authority did not want to issue a press release until its report was ready. Douglas Cross comments: 'If you have a car crash, you get the victims out first. You don't wait to make a report. By setting up the inquiry they gagged everyone for six weeks. The only leads we had were through two anonymous leaks.'

Even after the report appeared the action group was not happy with it. There was confusion about the quantity of aluminium sulphate involved. Less than a week after the publication of the report the water authority was forced to admit that the level of contamination was over three times higher than had been recorded. The report claimed that it was an 8 per cent solution. This figure was challenged by Cross; after intervention by the action group's solicitor it was revealed that this figure was the result of a confusion and that it should have been 26.8 per cent. The action group also criticizes the official report's analysis of the effects of the poisoning. This considered the possible medical effects of copper, zinc, aluminium and acidity, all in isolation. It then concluded that each one was not sufficient to cause serious health problems. The report did not dwell on the possible effects of a combination of these pollutants.

Overall, the official report plays down the risks. On the acidity of the water it says, 'Many carbonated drinks have a lower [pH] value.' On aluminium: 'Aluminium salts are abundant in nature, universally present in food and ... widely used in medical preparations.' Yet, as we have seen in an earlier chapter, there is growing concern about the dangers of aluminium in drinking water. The report also says, 'In medical terms the symptoms were relatively mild ... It has to be said that had there been no incident, there would have been a normal pattern of health problems. It is not possible to separate background problems from those caused by the incident.'

The local action group didn't like being told that their symptoms were 'relatively mild': for months after the incident Douglas Cross's wife was still unable to manage the five-minute walk into town because of her aggravated arthritis. Nor did they like being told that no health survey was planned of the likely long-term medical effects, such as a possibly increased risk of Alzheimer's Disease. Pending the results of a survey being carried out by Cornwall Health Authority, Douglas Cross and Dr Newman have carried out their own investigation of the immediate effects of the poisoning. Five hundred people filled in anonymous questionnaires. The results are indicated below.

Condition	Percentage of respondents
Sore mouth, tongue or throat	68
Feeling unwell or tired	63
Very thirsty	50
Stomach ache	48
Diarrhoea	38
Nausea and vomiting	38
Sore eyes	35
Mouth ulcers	23
Muscle cramps	23*
Increased pain of arthritis	22
Joint pain	21
Skin rashes, some very bad	18

* Cross had cramps after just one cup of water.

No one can prove that any one of these cases was caused by the drinking water. But if you extrapolate from this survey to estimate how many of the 6,000 people in the Camelford area may have suffered such symptoms, you get a figure of 4,000 people with sore mouths or throats, 2,880 with stomach ache, 2,280 with nausea and vomiting, 1,380 with muscle cramps and so on. That's a lot of illness in a small town. Douglas Cross also mentions some strange and disturbing individual incidents, such as the old lady in Delabole whose hands stuck to her face;

a policeman had to be called to help her. Such cases do not sound like 'background problems'.

These symptoms were probably caused by the acidity of the water, but what about the long-term effects of the aluminium, which, as we have seen, can build up in the brain and bones? Dr Neil Ward's independent report on the incident called it 'a major ecological disaster, the likes of which have not been recorded in Britain before'. As an expert on the toxicology of aluminium, he points up the potential long-term dangers of the poisoning: an increased incidence of arthritis, dementia and brittle-bone disease. The problem still hadn't gone away four months later. Some deposits of aluminium sulphate were left in pipes and have since been dislodged after mains pipe bursts. Local people say they suffer vomiting, arthritic pains and rashes again after each pipe burst. Nor are arthritic symptoms confined to the elderly. The mother of a four-year-old boy in Tintagel says he is unable to stand up because of joint pain after each repeated incident. No one can prove anything. But they know that when the water is a funny colour and tastes odd, they tend to get ill. Many local people remain extremely worried about possible effects on themselves, on their children and, in particular, on unborn foetuses. The acid dissolved other chemicals in pipes too: lead, copper and zinc. We have already dealt with the dangers of lead in water, and lead is a cumulative poison. Shouldn't someone be trying to predict what the problems will be in the future for the people of north Cornwall, so that something can be done about them now?

Because of a loophole in the law, a bizarre situation occurred: government pollution inspectors were able to sue only over the death of the fish, not the poisoning of the people. Those affected have to bring private prosecutions themselves. There are about 170 prosecutions being brought against the water authority. Another 100 people decided against legal action and have received an average of £260 in compensation from the water authority. It has been announced that those affected will also receive a 10 per cent water rate rebate. A police investigation into the whole affair has also begun.

John Lawrence made a number of recommendations in his

report. He criticized the practice of having keys that fit several locks on a site and of allowing a key out of the possession of the South West Water Authority staff: 'Responsibility lies with the operation and supervision of Lowermoor and particularly with the lax control of keys.' But he admitted that these recommendations were 'in the nature of closing the stable door after this particular horse has bolted'. An isolated incident, perhaps; but it could happen again. Because of financial restrictions, staff cuts have been made in water authorities nationwide, resulting in certain sites, such as Lowermoor, being left unmanned. 'All over the country jobs are being cut, systems are being automated, and that can result in accidents,' says Douglas Cross. John Lawrence agrees: 'Any claim that "It couldn't happen here" should initiate an independent examination by another manager.' He goes on to suggest that water authorities should copy a practice common in the chemical industry known as 'hazard study'. This involves looking at all possible failures, and combinations of failures, on paper to see what accidents might ensue and what improvements could be made to existing systems – a sort of 'worst-case scenario' for water. With something as important as drinking water, surely it is better to look at what might go wrong before it actually does?

9

THE DENTIST'S DREAM
Fluoridation of drinking water

Of course fluoride can be poisonous, and so can oxygen, and so can water. It is all a question of dosage.
Sir Cyril Clarke, Royal College of Physicians, 1987

Fluoride is added to water because it is intended to do us good. It does not treat the water in any way, nor does it make it cleaner or more pleasant to drink. It is added to improve the health of our teeth.

The British Fluoridation Society (BFS) exists to promote the artificial fluoridation of water in areas that are not already naturally high in fluoride. They claim that it is a great success. Fourteen-year-olds in fluoridated Birmingham, for instance, have 42 per cent less tooth decay than children of the same age in Bolton. Manchester five-year-olds have twice as much tooth decay as Newcastle five-year-olds; Newcastle is fluoridated. The BFS can point to ninety-five different studies, carried out in twenty countries, all of which have demonstrated that fluoridation works. No one knows precisely how fluoride helps teeth. Mike Lennon, chairman of the BFS, told us that there are a number of theories. The benefit may occur as fluoridated water passes over the teeth, or the fluoride may be absorbed by the body and incorporated into the teeth. Whichever theory is correct, the important thing is that tooth decay does seem to be reduced. Less tooth decay doesn't just mean fewer trips to the dentist. It also means fewer operations. In 1985 about 200,000 children under ten years old had to have a general anaesthetic for tooth extractions. A small amount of risk is always involved in such operations, and any reduction in their number is to be welcomed.

The BFS is not the only pressure group involved in the fluoride debate, however. Fluoridation is vigorously opposed by the National Anti-Fluoridation Campaign (NAFC). Both sides of this occasionally bitter argument can put up an impressive case, and both often flatly contradict each other. The NAFC points out that fluoride, in large doses, is a poison. It can be used as a garden insecticide or as a rat poison. If you take a large dose (i.e. about 2.5 grams) all at once, it will be fatal. If you swallow just 125 mg, you will become very ill. Large quantities are dangerous if they are inhaled, if they come into contact with skin or if they are swallowed, so bulk containers of the chemical have to be labelled as toxic. It's also dangerous to take a dose of, say, 20 mg a day or more over a long period of time. Such a dose causes rheumatic pains, dental decay, a permanently bent spine, bone deformations, excessive thirst and diarrhoea − a condition known as fluorosis. In one area of India, where a large number of villages have a naturally occurring high level of fluoride in water, about 350,000 people are affected in this way.[1] The amounts quoted above, however, are very much greater than those recommended for drinking water: 1 part per million (ppm) in our climate, 0.6 ppm in a tropical climate where people drink more water. Is there any danger at these lower levels? The NAFC says there is. It claims that teeth can become mottled even with a low exposure to fluoride. In Anglesey, after eleven years of fluoridation, an examination showed that 12 per cent of children's teeth had some mottled tooth enamel.

More important is the NAFC's concern that fluoridation may cause cancer. In 1975 Dr John A. Yiamouyiannis wrote a famous paper for the National Health Federation of America on cancer death rates in fluoridated and non-fluoridated cities, claiming that the death rate from cancer was far higher − up to 50 per cent higher in the case of some cancers − in cities where the water was artificially fluoridated. He concluded: 'Fluoride, in the amounts added to fluoridate public waters, causes cancer and/or increases the growth rates of cancer cells.' His colleague Dean Burk, formerly of the US National Cancer Institute, wrote in a letter to *Family Circle* magazine: 'Some 10 per cent of the 400,000 cancer deaths occurring per year in the US are linked with consumption of fluoridated water ... The health harms and increased cancer mortality induced by fluoridation are some ten times greater than that reported for asbestos exposure in Britain and the US, and greatly outweigh all proposed dental benefit.' He concluded dramatically that fluoridation was 'social mass murder'.

The NAFC also claims that fluoridation amounts to compulsory medication and that there is no way of guaranteeing people's intake, since water is not the only source of fluoride in the diet. It is present in toothpaste, for example, which children sometimes swallow, and in tea, instant coffee, cola and other soft drinks. If you drink a lot of tea in a fluoridated area, you could be consuming up to 8 mg of fluoride a day. Babies may also be at risk, the NAFC says, because they consume a lot of fluid in relation to their body weight. The mother's breast filters out fluoride, so a breast-fed baby receives only a tiny amount, but a bottle-fed baby in a fluoridated area will receive a great deal more.

Some opponents of fluoridation, rather surprisingly, say that it doesn't even help people's teeth. American dentist Casimir R. Sheft, in an article titled 'The Fluoridation Fiasco', wrote: 'There is not a single shred of scientific evidence that fluoride reduces tooth decay.'[2] He claims that in Ottawa, Kansas, after three years of fluoridation, tooth decay increased. In New York State dental teams found 50 per cent more children with dental defects in fluoridated Newburgh than in non-fluoridated Kingston.

As you would expect, the BFS has something to say about all this, and it has some impressive allies. As regards fluoride being a poison, it quotes Sir Cyril Clarke, director of the Royal College of Physicians' research unit: 'Of course fluoride can be poisonous, and so can oxygen, and so can water. It is all a question of dosage . . . There is no evidence that water containing approximately 1 ppm of fluoride in a temperate climate is associated with any harmful effect.'

As for mottled tooth enamel, this occurs in both fluoridated and non-fluoridated areas. In the fluoridated areas it is actually less common. A study comparing fluoridated Anglesey with non-fluoridated Leeds 'confirms previous findings that mottling is less common in fluoridated communities with 1 ppm than in non-fluoridated communities', say the BFS, the British Dental Association and the Health Educational Council.

Now for the allegations that fluoride causes cancer. The evidence of Drs Yiamouyiannis and Burk, cited above, sounds fairly convincing. But their work has been attacked by many other scientists. First, they didn't take account of any socio-economic factors in their study; in other words, they ignored probably the most important considerations of all in relation to cancer deaths. (To make a rather trivial comparison, it would be quite possible to produce a study showing that most people in hospital are ill. The conclusion could be drawn that if you don't want to get ill, you should avoid hospitals.) When their work was re-analysed in 1977, taking into account factors such as age and socio-economic status, it was stated that none of their evidence provided any reason to suppose that fluoridation is associated with an increase in cancer mortality, let alone that it causes cancer. The Knox Report, carried out by a Department of Health and Social Security working party under Professor Knox and published in 1985, said that Yiamouyiannis and Burk failed to compare like with like, made mistakes, introduced inconsistencies into their handling of data and failed to conduct acceptable tests of statistical significance. The American National Cancer Institute, for which Burk previously worked, has stated that it disagrees fundamentally with his and Yiamouyiannis's conclusions. It says, 'Fluoride or fluoride salts are not carcinogenic.' This conclusion is backed up by numerous independent scientists and statisticians. All say that there is no evidence that fluoride causes cancer.

As for the charge that it is compulsory medication, those in favour of fluoridation stress that it is a natural constituent of water. Lord Colwyn, a practising dentist, states, 'It is merely a process of supplementation or adjustment of most natural water to its optimum content, from the standpoint of public health.' And on the subject of the impossibility of determining what dose each person is getting, Mike Lennon of the BFS says that this was never the intention. 'The level of 1 ppm was based on observation of communities which already had fluoride occurring naturally at 1 ppm. At this level there could be seen to be maximum protection for teeth with no side-effects. Studies showed that there were no ill-effects on bottle-fed babies.'

So does fluoridation work? The BFS can produce plenty of statistics to show that it does. Although dental health has improved in all areas of Britain over the last twenty years, in fluoridated areas the improvement has been greater. In a booklet published in 1979 the British Dental Association, the BFS and the Health Education Council said, 'Studies in the US, New Zealand, the Netherlands and Great Britain have shown that fewer teeth were filled or extracted in fluoridated areas than in low-fluoride areas.' The benefits were felt not only by children; in naturally fluoridated Hartlepool 'In adults aged forty-five years and over there was a 44 per cent difference in the number of tooth sites attacked, demonstrating that fluoride in drinking water produces substantial lifelong benefits.' The USA has had fluoridation for thirty years. The first experiment was started in Grand Rapids, Michigan, in 1945. Here and elsewhere dental caries were reduced but 'No ill effects, either of a dental or medical nature, have been found.' It is, after all, a very direct way of helping everyone's teeth. Education programmes tend to help only those who take an interest, but with fluoridation the improvement crosses the class divide and everyone benefits.

But there is another objection to fluoride. P. Clavell Blount, chairman of the NAFC, claims that it is not dentistry or medical safety that is really at issue but individual liberty. 'It is the inherent, common law right of every adult of sound mind to decide for himself ... what he and his children will eat and drink ... Few will question people's right to choose.' Until the Water (Fluoridation) Act was passed in October 1985 it was not, strictly speaking, within the power of the water authorities to add fluoride to everyone's drinking water. Opponents of fluoridation regard the Act as an infringement of individual rights. They are incensed that the majority of MPs didn't vote on the Bill before it became law.

The BFS comments that we all sacrifice some liberty to fit in with society, such as driving on the left- or the right-hand side of a road. Fluoridation brings so many benefits that 'You would have to have a pretty strange view of personal liberty to want to deny everyone else those benefits just because you had a hang-up about it.' Lord Avebury, chairman of the Parliamentary Human Rights Committee, agrees with this attitude. 'The individual-liberty arguments against fluoridation are invalid, as can be judged from the fact that the issue has never been taken up by the National Council for Civil Liberties.'

The individual-liberty argument has held sway in other countries. Sweden, for instance, abolished fluoridation by Act of Parliament in 1971, mostly because it was felt to interfere with individual liberties. And, according to its Embassy, fluoridation was discontinued in the Netherlands in 1976, mainly for political reasons: 'Although the government was convinced of its benefit and safety, insufficient support was obtained in the second chamber to realize the necessary legislation.' The lobby opposing fluoridation in the Netherlands was particularly strong. Dr Hans Moolenburgh, one of its most vociferous members, gives an insight into opponents' thinking in his book *Fluoride: The Freedom Fight*: 'Precisely at the moment the state makes you swallow a medicine, without asking your permission and without the possibility of an alternative, democracy has ceased to be, and you live in a totalitarian state.' He is of the opinion that the reason why Dutch people fought against fluoridation was that they had been under an occupying force during the Second World War. 'Perhaps such a background gives a person an allergy to dictatorial measures.' He suggests that God was on their side: 'In the wings, however, there had been a Great Stage Manager . . . and He also made us win.'

Strong stuff. In Britain, with the exception of the pressure groups on both sides, fluoridation does not create so much excitement. Most people seem to be more or less in favour. When asked, 'Do you think fluoride should be added to water if it can reduce tooth decay?' between 65 and 75 per cent of respondents say yes.[3] Of course, anyone who has watched *Yes, Prime Minister* knows that opinion polls can be made to say what you want them to say. The opponents of fluoridation could rightly claim that if people were asked, 'Do you think a possibly dangerous chemical should be added to the water supply?' the answer would be a resounding no.

One undisputed fact to emerge from the polls is that most people don't know whether their water is fluoridated or not. The following areas *are* fluoridated: Birmingham, Solihull, Coventry, parts of Warwickshire, Worcestershire and Shropshire; Watford and parts of Bedfordshire; Newcastle, Gateshead, parts of Durham, North Tyneside, Northumberland and Cumbria (Hartlepool is naturally high in fluoride); parts of Humberside and Kirklees; parts of Lincolnshire, Nottinghamshire and Derbyshire; parts of Oxfordshire and Buckinghamshire; parts of Gwent, Gwynedd and Powys; the area around Crewe. Northern Ireland and Scotland are generally *not* fluoridated; nor are London, most other parts of the South-east, East Anglia, Wessex, the South-west, Lancashire or Greater Manchester. About one in ten people in this country has fluoridated water, at a current cost of about 13p per person per year. This money, say advocates of fluoridation, is more than saved in fewer fillings and extractions.

If your water is fluoridated and you don't want it to be, it is possible to buy a defluoridator – at a price. A company called Borderchain Ltd, in the West Midlands, manufactures a water-purification system for home use that, it claims, removes all fluoride. The system has to be fitted under the kitchen sink and, depending on the size, costs £300–800.

To take a step back for a moment: what causes tooth decay? In a word: sugar, in sweets, chocolate and sticky drinks. The government could do something about this, if it really wanted to. It could, for example, ban all sweet, chocolate and cola advertisements, and it could make all confectionery carry a government health warning. These measures would make the government look ridiculous to most people, however, and would force it into taking on Coca-Cola, Cadbury and British Sugar, among others. So instead it has opted for fluoride, which means people can have their cake and eat it – or, rather, that they can eat their cake and keep their teeth.

It is clear that, where fluoride is concerned, passions among campaigners run high. Opponents compare fluoride with Thalidomide or the Nazi Occupation; they use phrases such as 'compulsory mass medication' and 'social mass murder'. But they also receive their share of abuse and have been called a 'vociferous, ill-minded minority of persons'. Each side produces evidence to back up its argument. One produces a study to show that fluoride is linked with, for example, Down's Syndrome; the other side produces another study to show that there is no link.

Elsewhere in this book we have argued that where there is a serious doubt about a chemical in drinking water, we should err on the side of safety and work to remove it. But the evidence that pesticides, lead, aluminium and so on are dangerous is, in our opinion, much stronger than the evidence presented about the dangers of fluoride. Concern, or outright alarm, about other chemicals mentioned in this book is supported by an impressive range of national and international scientific and public-health organizations: the World Health Organization, the US Environmental Protection Agency, the British Medical Association, the US Food and Drug Administration, the US National Cancer Institute. Fluoridation is not opposed by any of these bodies; on the contrary, some encourage it. And unlike pesticides, lead or nitrates, which can do us no good at all, fluoride is of benefit to our teeth.

Following privatization, the debate may become academic. The chairman of Severn Trent Water Authority, John Bellack, said on the BBC's *P.M.* programme on 29 December 1988 that fluoride may be withdrawn from the water supply after privatization. He stated that it was a question of indemnity against possible personal injury cases. 'The risks are, as far as we know, as far as the government knows and as far as medical advisers say, non-existent. But, however minimal they may be, I have to be covered against them.'

10
PRIVATIZATION

The [privatization] proposals herald a major advance for the
protection of the water environment.
Department of the Environment, 1988

For us public health and hygiene are not matters to be dealt with by
market forces.
John Cunningham, Labour's Environment spokesman, 1988

On 5 February 1986 the government announced its intention
to privatize the ten water authorities of England and Wales.
Public water supplies in Northern Ireland and Scotland will be
unaffected. In July 1987 plans were also revealed for a National
Rivers Authority, a public regulatory body for the privatized
water industry. A draft Bill was introduced to Parliament on 11
November 1988. It detailed one of the largest privatization
programmes to date, involving the monopoly supply of the
basic necessity of life. Ninety-nine per cent of British households
receive mains drinking water, the highest proportion in the
world. The water industry's assets are valued at £27 billion,
dwarfing, for example, British Telecom's assets of £4 billion. In
1986–7 the ten water authorities to be privatized made total
profits of £530 million.

From its earliest suggestion the privatization of water has
come under fierce attack from an alliance of Opposition politicians, environmentalists and conservationists. We have already
criticized the current system of water management in this
country and believe that changes are desperately needed. The
Department of the Environment has told us, 'The [privatization]
proposals herald a major advance for the protection of the
water environment.' But is selling water to the private sector a
proper response to the current crisis?

Privatization is the culmination of a trend. Water-authority
managers have charted the politicization of their profession.

Take some of them out for a quiet, off-the-record chat and they will tell you that political interference has changed the nature of their job and threatened their commitment to drinking water quality. Executives who disagree with government policy tend not to remain long in their posts. At North West Water, we have been told, none of the managers who were known to oppose privatization remains on the staff.

In the 1970s the majority of water-authority board members were appointed by local authorities, and meetings were usually held in public. In the 1980s, however, things have changed. The government can now appoint the boards, and their meetings tend to be held in private. (Welsh Water is one honourable exception to this trend.) In the words of veteran campaigner and Liberal politician Des Wilson: 'It seems extraordinary that matters concerning the supply and quality of this basic commodity should be considered in secret.'

Tony Davies was the director of Scientific Services for Anglian Water between 1974 and 1983. Part of his function was to oversee water quality, and he spent much of his time charting the rising nitrate levels in East Anglian drinking water. Towards the end of his time with the water authority he noticed a 'considerable increase in the involvement and interference of government in the financial management of regional water authorities'. The 1983 Water Act gave the government powers to appoint water-authority board members. According to Tony Davies, the elected representatives on the boards soon disappeared. 'The regional water authority boards were then reorganized on government initiative, with nominated members only ... The net result of this has been an increase in the water rate that the public have been paying, with little or no improvement in the amount of money being spent to preserve and to protect the water-quality resources of the UK.'

If privatization does improve the situation, it is worth reflecting that, to a large extent, the current crisis has been caused by the build-up to privatization itself. In other words, making the water authorities financially attractive has damaged water quality already. According to Tony Davies, government action has pushed water-quality management lower and lower down the water authorities' agenda: 'When I retired, I was extremely concerned that there was a measurable decrease in the water quality of the rivers, and also of our groundwater, as a result of this imposition of a reduction in the borrowing requirement of regional water authorities.' As a science officer Tony Davies had an independent role within the water authority, but this role is now much weaker: 'There's been a cutback in the number of engineers and scientists employed in regional water authorities. There's been a cutback in the amount of research done. There's been an inordinately large increase in water rate with no benefit to the public, and, not least of all, there's been a reduction in public accountability because the elected members previously on the board no longer exist there.'

There were quiet rumblings in Parliament about changes in the water industry in the early 1980s. At a period when authorities were struggling to come to terms with new European rules concerning water quality, the House of Lords Select Committee concluded in 1982 that the level of funding for water research, including research into the health implications of drinking-water pollution, was too low. David Wheeler of the Robens Institute says, 'It is well known that the entire water industry is currently underfunded by at least £100 million per annum. Water authorities are subject to arbitrary and damaging external financing limits in order not to increase the Public Sector Borrowing Requirement. Thus it is unfair to blame water authorities for failing to meet standards; the criticism would be better aimed at those who set the investment limits.' One example is that in the late 1970s and early 1980s spending on new sewage works was cut drastically. It is now rising again, but it is still not at the level that was reached in the mid-1970s. As we have seen in a previous chapter, this is at a time when sewage works are ageing badly and having to cope with increasingly sophisticated chemical pollution.

South West Water is by now almost completely self-financing and making a profit. This makes it more attractive to the private investor, and the accountants are doubtless happy. But in order to reach this position water charges have risen above the rate of inflation; staff have been reduced by 25 per cent (staff shortages were a factor in the recent Cornwall pollution incident); complaints related to water supply are up 43 per cent in Devon; bacteriological failures are up to 33 per cent in certain districts; and sewage works are failing to meet their pollution consents 20 per cent of the time.[1] Quite a price to pay for a clean balance sheet. Throughout the country it is a similar story: spending projects have been squeezed to make the water companies more attractive for sale; borrowing has been cut back; and water charges have risen in the last six years by 24 per cent above the rate of inflation.

With politicization of the water business has come increasing secrecy, that curse of so much of British public life. When embarrassing facts have to be disclosed, flashy public relations techniques are employed to make bad appear really quite good. One annual report from Thames Water devotes less space to an examination of its record on water quality than to full-colour reproductions of two advertisements extolling the water authority's recent achievements. An Anglian Water annual report gave details of bacteriological standards but not of its difficulties in complying with EEC directives on nitrates and pesticides. Although several of Anglia's supplies fall below the EEC standards, all the report acknowledged was that 'At no time were EEC derogation limits exceeded.' In one of their reports Yorkshire Water provides no figures for chemical compliance, instead choosing to assert, 'In no case is there a danger to health.'

There is a striking contrast with the USA and its Freedom of Information Act. The powerful American Environmental Protection Agency, for which there is no British equivalent, can stimulate critical public reviews of water quality that would be almost inconceivable in Britain. American consumers must be notified of failures to meet drinking-water standards. British water authorities, on the other hand, frequently appear to want to minimize the public perception of such difficulties. Their first response to any water alert seems to be to offer bland assurances that all is well, even if they are not sure themselves, as happened in Cornwall and in the case of the river Dee incident. In truth, most consumers have no idea whether their supplies meet EEC standards, and even if they do know, nobody is studying, on a national scale, what their drinking water is doing to them.

One potentially positive effect of privatization is that we are promised more openness about water-quality data – although this is something that could be achieved without going to all the trouble of selling off the industry. Yet under the draft privatization Bill it will still be very difficult to prosecute water authorities for poisoning drinking water. After the Cornish incident, as we have mentioned, it emerged that water authorities could not be prosecuted for poisoning their consumers, only for killing fish. This loophole appears to remain in the new legislation. The new water companies themselves, conversely, are to be given extensive legal powers against consumers who transgress. Andrew Lees says, 'Under the draft Bill, massive private companies will be able to poison the water of entire cities without being prosecuted. But someone who fails to repair a dripping tap, or takes a kettle of water to a neighbour who has been cut off because she cannot afford to pay the bill, can be taken to court and fined.' Tony Davies is not impressed by what he has heard about the new system: 'What will happen when the water authorities are privatized? ... My informed guess would be that the quality of water at tap will deteriorate further. The protection and improvement of the quality of our vital water resources will suffer even more than they have done over the last eight to ten years.' And some water managers have voiced fears that there will be an inevitable conflict of interest between the natural commercial desire for profit and the obligation to protect the public health. Ron Packham, when president of the Institution of Water and Environmental Management, said that he was 'somewhat anxious' about privatization. He voiced concern about a possible 'conflict of interests between the interests of the shareholders and the interests of improved water. You can save money by letting the water quality deteriorate.'

The most important question of all is: who is going to act as policeman? The present system has many flaws, notably the fact that the water authorities are both poachers and gamekeepers. Following privatization it seems likely that most of the day-to-day monitoring of drinking-water quality will be undertaken by the privatized water utilities. There will be a greater role for district councils to play but probably no more money to allow them to carry out the regular monitoring that is necessary.

One genuinely hopeful development, however, is the planned National Rivers Authority (NRA). The NRA will be independent of the water companies and will police river pollution to ensure that potential polluters obey the law. It might be argued that what we really need is an independent body to police the whole water environment: surface water, groundwater, sea water and drinking water. Nevertheless, the NRA seems a step in the right direction. One water-authority official told us, 'We'll be considerably better off under an independent organization. At the moment, in many areas, the water authorities are the biggest polluters. They cause the pollution and attempt to regulate it. Although most try to carry out their duties properly, there's nothing like someone looking over your shoulder to concentrate the mind.'

There is, though, one big problem with the NRA, as with all water-quality enforcement in the private sector. Put bluntly, the looser the regulation, the better the chance of a politically successful privatization. The NRA will be only as good as the standards it is instructed to uphold. Friends of the Earth reports that the bankers who spoke at a water-privatization conference in 1987 stressed that over-regulation would reduce the attractiveness of investing in a new private water company. Andrew Lees believes that he has already spotted some backsliding by government ministers anxious to smooth the path to the sell-off: 'In July 1987, in a consultation document on the NRA, it was said that statutory river quality objectives [RQOs] would be set in the summer or autumn of 1988. But in 1988 a letter sent to the water authorities indicated that these statutory RQOs would not, in fact, be set until some time in 1990–91. The government has backtracked on a clear commitment to set these RQOs, and RQOs form the framework for the protection of the water environment. The government realizes that the higher the targets set for the water environment, and the more effective the monitoring of those targets, then the less money will be made when the water industry is privatized. In effect, the government has a vested interest in low standards at the moment.'

Industrialists are putting discreet pressure on the government not to set too high an environmental standard. Companies that buy water are worried that higher environmental standards will mean higher prices. Mr James Cropper, president of the Paper and Board Industry Federation, has said that industrialists are worried that they are 'going to pay a hell of a lot more . . . if the "green" lobby get their way in Parliament in terms of a big capital expenditure programme and all sorts of restrictions'.

As this book went to press the government was trying to stitch up a last-minute deal with the EEC over just what the new water companies will have to achieve in the way of water quality. The EEC Commissioner, Mr Carlo Ripa di Meana, has alarmed ministers by his refusal to accept planned exemptions from EEC standards. Without these exemptions, privatization could run into serious trouble. Water-authority executives wonder who will buy their shares if the EEC forces them to spend millions on a vast water clean-up. Likewise, who is going to want to buy shares in companies that regularly break European law? Carlo Ripa di Meana is a very powerful man at the moment and seems to be in no mood for compromise. Recently he said, 'I hope that the present situation in the UK will be put right. It is most disconcerting.' As usual, it seems that the interests of the British consumer are better served by the bureaucrats in Brussels than by the politicians in Whitehall.

Internal water-authority documents underline the industry's fears. They make it clear that senior executives are eager to do a deal with the EEC about a timetable for compliance with EEC water-quality standards. These documents – discovered, in all places, inside a Friends of the Earth recycling plant – also detail the industry's public relations plans. Some marketing genius suggests raising the profile of the water industry by getting a TV weatherman to drink a glass of water on air, sponsoring a 'Miss Wet T-shirt' competition in the *Sun* news-paper and other such inspired PR gimmicks. Altogether £20 million is being spent on PR and advertising. Using that money to clean up the water might be a better idea and – who knows? – might even be a better sales pitch.

Government ministers have presented privatization as 'green' legislation of great benefit to the consumer and the environment. But, as we have repeatedly seen, these self-same politicians have such a poor track record on water pollution that we can have little confidence in their apparent conversion to the environmentalist cause. If privatization really is a 'green' policy, why has it been opposed by a whole range of non-political conservationist organizations – such as the Countryside Commission, the Campaign for the Preservation of Rural England, the Ramblers Association, the Royal Society for the Protection of Birds, the National Anglers Council and the National Trust – organizations that are concerned about both water quality and the possibility that water companies will sell off recreational land to private developers?

It seems distinctly possible that the new private water companies will be granted wide discretion in tackling pollution from sources such as lead and nitrates. Labour's Environment spokesman, Jack Cunningham, claims that documents leaked to him by unhappy officials effectively exclude nitrate pollution as an indicator of water quality and state that lead should be allowed to reach 100 μg/l before remedial action is required. In the past, when faced with pollution standards, politicians have not hesitated to fudge the figures, move the goalposts, grant spurious exemptions and generally ignore the unmistakable signs of a sick water environment. These same politicians are drawing up the blueprints for the privatized water business of the future.

In the case of waste dumping, private industry already works, in theory, within a framework of government regulation. But, as we have seen, there are gaping loopholes in the law, a failure to police, a failure to enforce and widespread problems, all recognized by reputable waste-disposal companies and the chemical industry itself. The system is wide open to abuse. And this is the result of what politicians claim to be good regulation over private enterprise. In some respects the government is now suggesting that the same model should be applied to the whole water industry. It is hard to feel very confident, and few people do. According to a *Sunday Times*/MORI poll of December 1988, only 15 per cent of Britons support government policy on this issue.

One other problem for the new water companies will be that new pollutants are being identified all the time. In October 1988, for example, we suddenly learned that chemicals called polycyclic aromatic hydrocarbons (PAHs) were washing out of the coal-tar linings of some water mains and into drinking water. About 60 per cent of Britain's water mains have such linings – over 200,000 kilometres of underground pipework. The World Health Organization says that PAHs are 'potentially hazardous substances and exposure should be minimized'. Thames Water has estimated that it would cost £1 billion to clear coal-tar linings from its area alone. If it is found that PAHs are serious pollutants, who is going to pay for such remedial work on top of all the other urgently needed expenditure on sewage treatment, nitrate control and the like? Whatever happens, it is certain that water charges will have to rise sharply. In January 1989 water-authority chairmen told the Department of the Environment that prices would have to go up by well over the 12.5 per cent a year predicted by the government if progress were to be made towards meeting EEC standards for drinking water and beach cleaning.

At the heart of the privatization debate is a moral argument. Water is not like British Steel or Jaguar cars. It is the mainstay of our environment and fundamental to human health. Many people believe that the provision of wholesome water at a reasonable cost is too important to be left to commercial considerations. Conflicts must surely arise between the public health and the corporate balance sheet. It was this very issue that led the Victorians to make the provision of water a public undertaking in the first place. Politicians have starved the water industry of funds, encouraged it to evade environmental standards and distorted its priorities in the run up to privatization.

These same politicians would now have us believe that private enterprise will clean up the mess they have created. It is hard to disagree with the words of Labour's Environment spokesman John Cunningham, who told Parliament: 'We do not believe that an essential resource such as water should be managed and sold for private gain. For us public health and hygiene are not matters to be dealt with by market forces.'

11
CONSUMER ACTION

A small group can achieve a lot.
Myra Garrett, Tower Hamlets Federation of Tenants, 1988

We think people should be alarmed by the way in which our water environment is treated and by the cavalier attitude to the many threatening poisons on tap. We believe that most people would prefer to drink cleaner water, enjoy cleaner rivers, holiday on safer beaches and live in an altogether less toxic environment. So what can the individual do about it?

First, the water in your own home. Never be tempted to save time by filling the kettle from the hot tap; hot water dissolves minerals such as lead from the pipes far more easily than cold. Second, flushing the pipes in the morning – that is, letting the water run for a couple of minutes before you use it – will ensure that the water you drink comes direct from the mains and hasn't been standing around in your pipes all night picking up chemicals. Third, fill your kettle afresh each time you boil water. Repeated boiling of water concentrates the chemicals in it.

If you want to know more about what is coming out of your kitchen tap, contact the supplier for information.

There are alternatives to the kitchen tap. You can drink bottled water, for example. Millions of people do. Sales of bottled water have trebled since 1983. Britons now drink 150 million bottles a year. Some labels indicate the mineral content of the water, and if you have a degree in chemistry, you may be able to work out which is best for you. The rest of us have to take it on trust that the water is purer than what comes out of the tap, since bottled water is not subject to the same official quality standards as tap water. The *Which?* report in February 1989 found that 'Chemically, bottled waters may be purer than some tap water. But several brands did much worse than tap water in bacteriological terms.' Some of the still mineral waters contained more than 10,000 bacteria per millilitre; the sparkling waters were generally better. *Which?* warned that any water for a baby's feed should always be boiled first. The main disadvantage, however, is the cost of using large quantities for making tea, diluting children's orange squash and cooking.

Another option is to use a water filter. There are two main types – the jug type from about £9 and the permanent under-sink type from £50 to 800. Most manufacturers say that their filters will improve the taste of water and provide 'crystal-clear, spring-fresh drinking water'. Some make more specific claims about the contaminants that their filters will remove. A typical claim is that they will 'reduce lead, nitrates and pesticides'. But, again, there is no official quality control on these filters, and so far there have been few independent studies of their efficiency. One study, carried out for BBC Radio 4's *Food Programme* in October 1988, was fairly small and was restricted to testing how efficiently filters removed lead and nitrate. It took a random sample of the water filters available (see opposite). The prices do not include the cost of filters (in the case of the first three) or of plumbing in (in the case of the last three). In the case of Aquaguard the cartridge to treat nitrate costs £44.22 and the lead-treating cartridge £44.74. The BBC study carried the following disclaimer: 'Although every effort has been made to ensure the accuracy of this report, no liability as to its accuracy can be accepted by The Polytechnic of Central London or The British Broadcasting Corporation.'

Which? magazine looked at jug filters in its February 1989 report. It found that, by and large, the filters lived up to the manufacturers' claims. All the filters tested were good at removing lead, solvents and PAHs from water. The amounts of aluminium and nitrates removed were more variable.

If you do buy a filter, be sure to change the cartridge when it has filtered the amount of water recommended by the manufacturer. Also be wary of door-to-door water-filter salesmen. There have been reports of people being talked into purchasing expensive, and possibly inefficient, filter systems by fast-talking salesmen. If you are seriously interested in buying a filter, ask

Filter	Cost (1988)	Percentage of lead removed	Percentage of nitrate removed
Waymaster Crystal	£9.95	60	88
Brita	£11.95	26	No data available
Filtaware	£10.95	No data available	Over 96
Kleen Plus Reverse Osmosis Machine	£65.00	76	46
Aquaguard No. TGC10	See p.116	90	Over 96
Bruner Nitrate Removal Unit	£690	90	Over 96

for quotes from several established dealers, and make sure you are given a guarantee.

A final word of warning: don't leave either filtered or bottled water standing around in a warm place. Keep both refrigerated, otherwise bacteria will have a chance to multiply.

Filters and bottles are short-term measures. You may feel, as we do, that they should not be necessary. Pure and wholesome drinking water should be available to everybody. To bring this about, and to protect the wider water environment, you have to campaign.

The best way to do this is to join an organization such as Greenpeace or Friends of the Earth. Greenpeace can be contacted at Freepost, 30–31 Islington Green, London N1 8BR. Friends of the Earth produces a free leaflet called 'How to Find Out About Your Tap Water – and Complain if It's Substandard'. Not only does it tell you exactly what the title suggests but it also describes briefly the pollutants that may be in your water and states the legal limit for each one. Friends of the Earth even provides a form for a complaint to the EEC. It has also launched a 'Charter for the Water Environment', calling for improvements in the way we treat our most valuable resource, on which it would like to gather as many signatures as possible. For both of these write to Friends of the Earth, 26–28 Underwood Street, London N1 7JQ.

You can also make sure you contribute as little as possible to water pollution. *The Green Consumer Guide*, mentioned in the reading list, is invaluable. You may like to try 'ECOVER' products, washing and cleaning materials that are fully bio-degradable: far more environment-friendly.

It is quite possible for individuals, or small groups of people, to get things moving at a high level. Myra Garrett, of the Tower Hamlets Federation of Tenants, told us how they took action on the quality of their water. Following many complaints that the water tasted bad, smelled funny and was cloudy, the Federation of Tenants decided to have the water tested. On finding that it contained a worryingly high level of nitrites, which have been linked with stomach cancer, they wrote to Thames Water. The water authority told them that there was 'no significant health hazard', even though levels of gastric cancer in Tower Hamlets are high. The group then wrote a letter to the EEC, with the help of their local Member of the European Parliament. In April 1986 their letter was registered as an official complaint in the Commission's files. A subsequent test showed that the nitrite levels had been reduced. Myra Garrett: 'I was impressed that we, as a small group, could influence people at a fairly high level to take action. A small group can achieve a lot.'

Some local councillors are also keen to help with environmental issues. A 'Clean Rivers Campaign' in the Derbyshire area, started by Greenpeace, is now partly funded by Derbyshire County Council. Why not ask your local councillor if he or she is doing anything to protect your water environment and to improve the quality of your drinking water the next time you are asked for your vote? You could ask your MP the same question. Or else get campaigning yourself. All over the country there are groups interested in preserving the environment. It's up to us all to make sure they succeed.

APPENDIX
The polluted-beach league

Holidaymakers will find that the latest results of tests on the officially designated bathing beaches in England, Northern Ireland and Wales make depressing reading. One in three has a level of sewage pollution in excess of EEC limits. Dirtiest areas are the north-west, the south coast and Northumberland. These breaches of EEC law leave the British government open to prosecution, but the Commissioner has accepted a commitment to meet limits by the mid-1990s, at a cost of over £500 million. The debate will continue as to whether it is really safe to bathe in any sewage-polluted water, even that which meets the EEC standard. In the meantime readers may appreciate a list of those beaches that failed in 1988.

Anglian: *pass* 19, *fail* 9: Cleethorpes, Sutton on Sea, Heacham, Hunstanton Beach, Sheringham, Cromer, Great Yarmouth Pier, Great Yarmouth South, Dovercourt.

Thames: *pass* 0, *fail* 2: Southend Thorpe Bay, Southend West-cliff Bay.

Yorkshire: *pass* 21, *fail* 1: Flamborough South Landing.

Northumbrian: *pass* 9, *fail* 10: Spittal, Newbiggin, South Beach/Seaton Sluice, Whitley Bay, Marsden, Roker/Whitburn, Seaham, Crimdon, Seaton Carew, Saltburn.

Southern: *pass* 27, *fail* 38: Herne Bay, Joss Bay, Broadstairs, Ramsgate, Sandwich Bay, Deal Castle, Folkestone, Sandgate, Hythe, Dymchurch, St Mary's Bay, Littlestone, Hastings, Seaford, Newhaven, Brighton, Hove, Southwick, South Lancing, Worthing, Littlehampton, Middleton-on-Sea, Pagham, Selsey, Eastney, Southsea, Calshot, Milford-on-Sea, Christchurch Bay, Colwell Bay, Gurnard, Cowes, Ryde, Seagrove, St Helens, Bembridge, Whitecliff Bay, Ventnor.

Wessex (south coast): *pass* 26, *fail* 1: Christchurch–Avon Beach.

South-west: *pass* 92, *fail* 17: Lyme Regis, Shaldon, Paignton, Salcombe South Sands, Thurlestone, Plymouth Hoe, Seaton (Cornwall), Charlestown and Duporth, Penewan, Porthallow, Porthleven, Marazion and Mounts Bay, Porth Gwidden, Trevone Bay, Bude, Instow, Combe Martin.

Wessex (Bristol Channel): *pass* 4, *fail* 7: Minehead Terminus, Dunster North West, Burham Jetty, Berrow, Weston-super-Mare Uphill slipway, Weston-super-Mare Grand Pier, Clevedon swimming-pool.

Welsh: *pass* 37, *fail* 11: Jacksons Bay Barry, Whitmore Bay Barry, Cold Knap Barry, Southerndown, Sandy Bay Porthcawl, Swansea Bay, Tenby North, Abersoch, Llandudno West Shore, Kinmel Bay, Rhyl.

North-west: *pass* 6, *fail* 27: Formby, Ainsdale, Southport, St Anne's, St Anne's North, Blackpool South, Blackpool Central, Blackpool North, Bispham, Cleveleys, Fleetwood, Heysham–Half Moon Bay, Morecambe South, Morecambe North, Bardsea, Aldingham, Newbiggin, Walney West Shore, Roan Head, Askam-in-Furness, Haverigg, Seascale, St Bees, Allonby South, Allonby, Silloth, Skinburness.

N. Ireland: *pass* 14, *fail* 2: Ballycastle, Newcastle.

Happy holidays.

NOTES

1 Fresh fields and poisons new

1. Estimate from James Erlichman, *Gluttons for Punishment*, Harmondsworth, Penguin, 1986.
2. According to the London Food Commission in 'Pesticide Residues in Food', 1986.
3. Recounted in Erlichman, *Gluttons for Punishment*.
4. According to the Water Authorities Association in 'Water Pollution from Farm Waste in 1987', 1988.
5. ibid.
6. Figures from the Fertilizer Manufacturers' Association.
7. Figures quoted by the Agriculture Minister, John MacGregor, January 1989.

2 The poison in the pipes

1. An assessment, based on the best available information, by Professor Derek Bryce-Smith, head of the Department of Organic Chemistry at Reading University.
2. ibid.

4 The dustbin of Europe

1. Estimate in 'Not in My Backyard', Greenpeace, 1987.
2. Second report of the Hazardous Waste Inspectorate, July 1986.

5 The age of consents

1. Information from *Environmental Data Services* magazine, August 1988, based on water-authority figures.

2. Information from Andrew Lees of Friends of the Earth, based on water-authority figures.

6 *Moving the goalposts*

1. Quoted by the Robens Institute, Surrey University, in its evidence to the House of Commons Select Committee on pollution of rivers and estuaries. Other information in this chapter is drawn from this source.
2. Estimate by Friends of the Earth.

9 *The dentist's dream*

1. Information from *India Today*, May 1986.
2. From the October 1982 issue of the US publication *Flouridation News*.
3. British Fluoridation Society, 'Fluoridation Action Report', 1987.

10 *Privatization*

1. Information contained in Friends of the Earth's evidence to the House of Commons Select Committee on the environment, March 1987.

FURTHER READING

John Elkington and Julia Hailes, *The Green Consumer Guide*, London, Gollancz, 1988

James Erlichman, *Gluttons for Punishment*, Harmondsworth, Penguin, 1986

Andrew Lees and Karen McVeigh, 'An Investigation of Pesticide Pollution in Drinking Water in England and Wales', available from the Friends of the Earth's Water and Toxics Campaign

London Food Commission, *Food Adulteration and How to Beat It*, London, Unwin Hyman, new edition to be published 1989

The Marine Conservation Society, *The Good Beach Guide*, London, Ebury Press, New Edition to be published 1989

C. Pye-Smith and C. Hall (eds.), *The Countryside We Want: A Manifesto for the Year 2000*, Hartland, Devon, Green Books, 1987

INDEX

FOR THE BEST IN PAPERBACKS, LOOK FOR THE

In every corner of the world, on every subject under the sun, Penguin represents quality and variety – the very best in publishing today.

For complete information about books available from Penguin – including Pelicans, Puffins, Peregrines and Penguin Classics – and how to order them, write to us at the appropriate address below. Please note that for copyright reasons the selection of books varies from country to country.

In the United Kingdom: Please write to *Dept E.P., Penguin Books Ltd, Harmondsworth, Middlesex, UB7 0DA*

If you have any difficulty in obtaining a title, please send your order with the correct money, plus ten per cent for postage and packaging, to *PO Box No 11, West Drayton, Middlesex*

In the United States: Please write to *Dept BA, Penguin, 299 Murray Hill Parkway, East Rutherford, New Jersey 07073*

In Canada: Please write to *Penguin Books Canada Ltd, 2801 John Street, Markham, Ontario L3R 1B4*

In Australia: Please write to the *Marketing Department, Penguin Books Australia Ltd, P.O. Box 257, Ringwood, Victoria 3134*

In New Zealand: Please write to the *Marketing Department, Penguin Books (NZ) Ltd, Private Bag, Takapuna, Auckland 9*

In India: Please write to *Penguin Overseas Ltd, 706 Eros Apartments, 56 Nehru Place, New Delhi, 110019*

In Holland: Please write to *Penguin Books Nederland B.V., Postbus 195, NL–1380AD Weesp, Netherlands*

In Germany: Please write to *Penguin Books Ltd, Friedrichstrasse 10–12, D–6000 Frankfurt Main 1, Federal Republic of Germany*

In Spain: Please write to *Longman Penguin España, Calle San Nicolas 15, E–28013 Madrid, Spain*

In France: Please write to *Penguin Books Ltd, 39 Rue de Montmorency, F-75003, Paris, France*

In Japan: Please write to *Longman Penguin Japan Co Ltd, Yamaguchi Building, 2–12–9 Kanda Jimbocho, Chiyoda-Ku, Tokyo 101, Japan*

A CHOICE OF PENGUINS

A Better Class of Person   John Osborne

The playwright's autobiography, 1929–56. 'Splendidly enjoyable' – John Mortimer. 'One of the best, richest and most bitterly truthful autobiographies that I have ever read' – Melvyn Bragg

Out of Africa   Karen Blixen (Isak Dinesen)

After the failure of her coffee-farm in Kenya, where she lived from 1913 to 1931, Karen Blixen went home to Denmark and wrote this unforgettable account of her experiences. 'No reader can put the book down without some share in the author's poignant farewell to her farm' – *Observer*

In My Wildest Dreams   Leslie Thomas

The autobiography of Leslie Thomas, author of *The Magic Army* and *The Degrest and the Best*. From Barnardo boy to original virgin soldier, from apprentice journalist to famous novelist, it is an amazing story. 'Hugely enjoyable' – *Daily Express*

The Winning Streak   Walter Goldsmith and David Clutterbuck

Marks and Spencer, Saatchi and Saatchi, United Biscuits, G.E.C. . . The U.K.'s top companies reveal their formulas for success, in an important and stimulating book that no British manager can afford to ignore.

Mind Tools   Rudy Rucker

Information is the master concept of the computer age, which throws a completely new light on the age-old concepts of space and number, logic and infinity. In *Mind Tools* Rudy Rucker has produced the most charming and challenging intellectual carnival since *Gödel, Escher, Bach*.

Bird of Life, Bird of Death   Jonathan Evan Maslow

In the summer of 1983 Jonathan Maslow set out to find the quetzal. In doing so, he placed himself between the natural and unnatural histories of Central America, between the vulnerable magnificence of nature and the terrible destructiveness of man. 'A wonderful book' – *The New York Times Book Review*

A CHOICE OF PENGUINS

Adieux: A Farewell to Sartre   Simone de Beauvoir

A devastatingly frank account of the last years of Sartre's life, and his death, by the woman who for more than half a century shared that life. 'A true labour of love, there is about it a touching sadness, a mingling of the personal with the impersonal and timeless which Sartre himself would surely have liked and understood' – *Listener*

Business Wargames   James Barrie

How did BMW overtake Mercedes? Why did Laker crash? How did MacDonalds grab the hamburger market? Drawing on the tragic mistakes and brilliant victories of military history, this remarkable book draws countless fascinating parallels with case histories from industry world-wide.

Metamagical Themas   Douglas R. Hofstadter

This astonishing sequel to the bestselling, Pulitzer Prize-winning *Gödel, Escher, Bach* swarms with 'extraordinary ideas, brilliant fables, deep philosophical questions and Carrollian word play' – Martin Gardner

Into the Heart of Borneo   Redmond O'Hanlon

'Perceptive, hilarious and at the same time a serious natural-history journey into one of the last remaining unspoilt paradises' – *New Statesman* 'Consistently exciting, often funny and erudite without ever being over-whelming' – *Punch*

The Assassination of Federico García Lorca   Ian Gibson

Lorca's 'crime' was his antipathy to pomposity, conformity and intoler-ance. His punishment was murder. Ian Gibson reveals the truth about Lorca's death and the atmosphere in Spain that allowed it to happen.

The Secrets of a Woman's Heart   Hilary Spurling

The later life of Ivy Compton-Burnett 1920–69. 'A biographical triumph . . . elegant, stylish, witty tender, immensely acute – dazzles and exhila-rates . . . a great achievement' – Kay Dick in the *Literary Review*. 'One of the most important literary biographies of the century' – *New Statesman*

Fantastic Invasion Patrick Marnham

Explored and exploited, Africa has carried a different meaning for each wave of foreign invaders – from ivory traders to aid workers. Now, in the crisis that has followed Independence, which way should Africa turn? 'A courageous and brilliant effort' – Paul Theroux

Jean Rhys: Letters 1931–66
Edited by Francis Wyndham and Diana Melly

'Eloquent and invaluable . . . her life emerges, and with it a portrait of an unexpectedly indomitable figure' – Marina Warner in the *Sunday Times*

Among the Russians Colin Thubron

One man's solitary journey by car across Russia provides an enthralling and revealing account of the habits and idiosyncrasies of a fascinating people. 'He sees things with the freshness of an innocent and the erudition of a scholar' – *Daily Telegraph*

The Amateur Naturalist Gerald Durrell with Lee Durrell

'Delight . . . on every page . . . packed with authoritative writing, learning without pomposity . . . it represents a real bargain' – *The Times Educational Supplement*. 'What treats are in store for the average British household' – *Books and Bookmen*

The Democratic Economy Geoff Hodgson

Today, the political arena is divided as seldom before. In this exciting and original study, Geoff Hodgson carefully examines the claims of the rival doctrines and exposes some crucial flaws.

They Went to Portugal Rose Macaulay

An exotic and entertaining account of travellers to Portugal from the pirate-crusaders, through poets, aesthetes and ambassadors, to the new wave of romantic travellers. A wonderful mixture of literature, history and adventure, by one of our most stylish and seductive writers.

The Diary of Virginia Woolf
Five volumes edited by Quentin Bell and Anne Olivier Bell

'As an account of intellectual and cultural life of our century, Virginia Woolf's diaries are invaluable; as the record of one bruised and unquiet mind, they are unique' – Peter Ackroyd in the *Sunday Times*

Voices of the Old Sea   Norman Lewis

'I will wager that *Voices of the Old Sea* will be a classic in the literature about Spain' – *Mail on Sunday* 'Limpidly and lovingly Norman Lewis has caught the helpless, unwitting, often foolish, but always hopeful village in its dying summers, and saved the tragedy with sublime comedy' – *Observer*

The First World War   A J P Taylor

In this superb illustrated history, A J P Taylor 'manages to say almost everything that is important for an understanding and, indeed, intellectual digestion of that vast event . . . A special text . . . a remarkable collection of photographs' – *Observer*

Ninety-Two Days   Evelyn Waugh

With characteristic honesty Evelyn Waugh here debunks the romantic notions attached to rough travelling; his journey in Guiana and Brazil is difficult, dangerous and extremely uncomfortable, and his account of it is witty and unquestionably compelling.

When the Mind Hears   Harlan Lane
A History of the Deaf

'Reads like a suspense novel . . . what emerges is evidence of a great wrong done to a minority group, the deaf' – *The New York Times Book Review* 'Impassioned, polemical, at times even virulent . . . (he shows) immense scholarship, powers of historical reconstruction, and deep empathy for the world of the deaf' – Oliver Sacks in *The New York Review of Books*

Beyond the Blue Horizon   Alexander Frater

The romance and excitement of the legendary Imperial Airways East-bound Empire service – the world's longest and most adventurous scheduled air route – relived fifty years later in one of the most original travel books of the decade. 'The find of the year' – *Today*

Voyage through the Antarctic   Richard Adams and Ronald Lockley

Here is the true, authentic Antarctic of today, brought vividly to life by Richard Adams, author of *Watership Down*, and Ronald Lockley, the world-famous naturalist. 'A good adventure story, with a lot of information and a deal of enthusiasm for Antarctica and its animals' – *Nature*

Getting to Know the General   Graham Greene

'In August 1981 my bag was packed for my fifth visit to Panama when the news came to me over the telephone of the death of General Omar Torrijos Herrera, my friend and host . . .' 'Vigorous, deeply felt, at times funny, and for Greene surprisingly frank' – *Sunday Times*

The Search for the Virus   Steve Connor and Sharon Kingman

In this gripping book, two leading *New Scientist* journalists tell the remarkable story of how researchers discovered the AIDS virus and examine the links between AIDS and lifestyles. They also look at the progress being made in isolating the virus and finding a cure.

Arabian Sands   Wilfred Thesiger

'In the tradition of Burton, Doughty, Lawrence, Philby and Thomas, it is, very likely, the book about Arabia to end all books about Arabia' – *Daily Telegraph*

When the Wind Blows   Raymond Briggs

'A visual parable against nuclear war: all the more chilling for being in the form of a strip cartoon' – *Sunday Times* 'The most eloquent anti-Bomb statement you are likely to read' – *Daily Mail*

A CHOICE OF PENGUINS

Trail of Havoc Patrick Marnham

In this brilliant piece of detective work, Patrick Marnham has traced the steps of Lord Lucan from the fateful night of 7th November 1974 when he murdered his children's nanny and attempted to kill his ex-wife. As well as being a fascinating investigation, the book is also a brilliant portrayal of a privileged section of society living under great stress.

Light Years Gary Kinder

Eduard Meier, an uneducated Swiss farmer, claims since 1975 to have had over 100 UFO sightings and encounters with 'beamships' from the Pleiades. His evidence is such that even the most die-hard sceptics have been unable to explain away the phenomenon.

And the Band Played On Randy Shilts
Politics, people and the AIDS epidemic

Written after years of extensive research by the only American journalist to cover the epidemic full-time, the book is a masterpiece of reportage and a tragic record of mismanaged institutions and scientific vendettas, of sexual politics and personal suffering.

The Return of a Native Reporter Robert Chesshyre

Robert Chesshyre returned to Britain from the United States in 1985 where he had spent four years as the *Observer*'s correspondent. This is his devastating account of the country he came home to: intolerant, brutal, grasping and politically and economically divided. It is a nation, he asserts, struggling to find a role.

Women and Love Shere Hite

In this culmination of *The Hite Report* trilogy, 4,500 women provide an eloquent testimony of the disturbingly unsatisfying nature of their emotional relationships and point to what they see as the causes. *Women and Love* reveals a new cultural perspective in formation: as women change the emotional structure of their lives, they are defining a fundamental debate over the future of our society.